M000049685

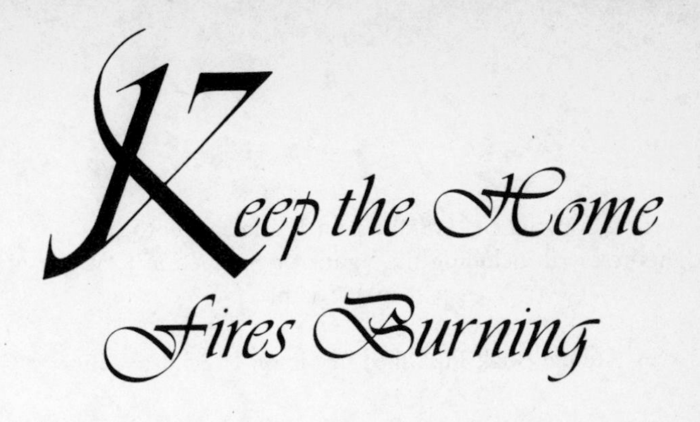

How to Have
an Affair with
Your Spouse

ANN
PEARLMAN
HINTON

A FIRESIDE BOOK
Published by Simon & Schuster, Inc. New York

A Fireside Book Published by Simon & Schuster, Inc.

Simon & Schuster Building
Rockefeller Center
1230 Avenue of the Americas
New York, New York 10020

Designed by Jennie Nichols/Levavi & Levavi
Manufactured in the United States of America

1 3 5 7 9 10 8 6 4 2

Library of Congress Cataloging in Publication Data

Hinton, Ann Pearlman.
Keep the home fires burning.

"A Fireside book."
1. Sex in marriage. I. Title.
HQ31.H494 1985 613.9'6 84-27645
ISBN: 0-671-55255-4

ACKNOWLEDGMENTS

I want to acknowledge the many people who helped me write this book. Especially, I want to thank my agent, Peter Ginsburg, who was enthusiastic about this project from its inception, and Barbara Gess, my editor, whose valuable suggestions were incorporated.

Shelley Aspaklaria convinced me to embark on this project during my pregnancy, and the results of our conversations and brainstorming sessions are seen on these pages. Linda Sherby, Ph.D., was always available and eager to read this in all its elementary stages, discussing ideas, offering excellent criticism, and being, as usual, supportive and loving. I also used the expertise of M. Susan Schneberger, A.C.S.W., whose knowledge of sex, illness, and the handicapped was extensive. Discussions with Gail Farley, Ph.D., particularly on fantasy and the unconscious connection between couples, helped clarify my thinking. Mel Barclay, M.D., generously shared his medical knowledge and experience and verified my medical facts. And I want to thank all the couples and individuals whom I have seen in therapy, because surely the knowledge I have gained working with them is on these pages.

For my husband . . .

CONTENTS

INTRODUCTION

Allison and Aaron were lying in bed, the bedroom TV tuned to Johnny Carson. Allison's head was in its usual cuddling place on Aaron's shoulder, and Aaron's arm was wrapped around her as they listened to the TV. Aaron began caressing her, his invitation clear. She draped her leg around his body, pushing up against him, offering her acceptance. Their caresses intensified and he entered her. As they rocked automatically, part of Allison was attuned to her own body and part of her was still listening to the Carson show. Carson made a one-liner that Allison found hysterically funny and she laughed. Later, after they had both come, Aaron quipped, "Someone said that making love was sex with the TV off. Now I know what he meant. I guess we just had sex." Hurt, and feeling slightly insulted, Allison snapped, "Yeah, well, more babies have been conceived to Johnny Carson than at any other time—except during the New York blackout."

The sex had been efficient. Their bodies, knowing how to satisfy themselves and please the other after so many years of coupling, produced orgasms with the least effort in the shortest possible time.

Fifteen years ago when they had met, they could hardly keep their hands off each other, so deep was their passion, so intense their lust, so thrilling the fact that they had found each other. They made love over and over again, exploring every pore, every crevice, every nerve ending. They pushed each other to their sexual limits and delved into varieties and possibilities they had only dimly known existed. When they were together, there was a feeling of sanctuary as both of them tossed off the cares of the day and devoted total attention to each other. It had seemed like a perfect relationship—passionate, lustful, tender, creative. Allison thought she had found the complete lover in Aaron and imagined that they would have decades of passion as they built their lives together. Aaron felt that Allison's lovemaking was ideal for him; he had found an exciting woman, one who made him feel complete, powerful, a person with whom he could express himself openly and totally.

Yet during the fifteen years they had spent together something had changed in the relationship. Not that sex wasn't good—their bodies melded perfectly, anticipating the subtle changes of feeling. But sex was always in the missionary position, usually on Wednesday and Saturday nights. Making love had become another part of the weekly routine, scheduled into cooking meatloaf for Monday's dinner, driving their son to his violin lesson, picking up their daughter at gymnastics, and watching the Carson show. The pleasure they could give each other was so guaranteed it had become almost automatic.

This was not what either of them had wanted. They had wanted their sexual relationship to grow with them, to stay as exciting as their lives while they adventured in the world. As Allison thought about this she wondered if it were possible to keep a sexual relationship exciting and intense when so much time with your lover was devoted to mutual support, to listening to problems, and to sharing responsibilities. Did concern about the mundane and the ordinary kill romance and passion? Or was it an inevitable erosion with time? Could the same body she saw vomiting, feverish, or farting remain sexually enthralling after two or three decades? Were a sexually passionate relationship and marriage mutually exclusive?

Keep the Home Fires Burning answers Allison's questions. It speaks to countless couples who do not want to sacrifice the excitement of a thrilling sexual relationship for the safety, companionship, and security of marriage. It is for those of you who are desirous of continuing to explore your sexuality and the sexuality of your lover over the decades that stretch before you.

In this society you, the long-term couple, may feel sexually "second class." You may feel that by being in a long-term marital relationship you are cheated. Monogamy in today's society has been besieged on all sides. Some of you may feel as though you're missing the "gusto" in life unless you're sampling a variety of different partners. You may feel you are unadventurous, stodgy, or old-fashioned if you don't become involved in extrasexual interludes. There are messages saying sex is recreational, fun, proof of our worth, our sense of self. Jump in! Enjoy! Partake! Explore the thrilling new world of nonintimate sex.

But sacrifices are made as we pursue recreational sex. For some of you, sex may have become another contest, another push for proficiency. You may seek a marathon of orgasms, couplings, and partners. Perhaps sex has become another status symbol. You may have lost the ability to be intimate sexually as sex becomes a performance done to or for, rather than with, someone. It is sad to think that during sex you feel as if you are a spectator, a performer, instead of a coupler. When you are more concerned with your own performance than with the sharing, you may feel alienated and alone.

The other trade-offs in your sampling of various sexual partners are well known. The excitement of a new partner brings the fear of rejection, the gnaw of performance anxiety, concerns about bodily appearance. Worse yet are the anxieties about penicillin-resistant VD or AIDS. Millions of you are terrified of giving or getting herpes, so that each new sexual experience brings anxious waiting for assurance that you have not contacted a chronic disease. When you wake up with someone you know only slightly, you may feel increasingly empty; then anonymous or recreational sex may strike you as tedious rather than pleasurable. There is a growing realization that you can't have it all. Recreational, fun sex with a variety of partners and sex as part of a long-term, loving relationship are mutually exclusive life choices. Some of you are committed to one or the other throughout your lives; others of you explore the glories of each at different times in your lives. But you may not have the safety, security, and comfort of a monogamous relationship and, at the same time, the thrill and excitement of embarking on new sexual relationships.

So each ideal survives. One is made more possible, more acceptable, by the sexual revolution; the other is the traditional, long-honored choice. Almost half of American spouses remain faithful, and many more of you hold this as a goal, crushed only by your appetite for a variety of sexual experiences. It is a testament to the seduction of the pair bond that, in spite of skyrocketing divorce rates, in spite of the temptations thrown at us from the media and the workplace, monogamy still survives as an ideal.

It is clear, too, for you, the long-term couple, that a pleasure bond has grown between you. You know each other intimately; your lives are interwoven and mutually dependent. Your lover's body is almost as familiar as your own. You can anticipate your mate's delight and sexual readiness. You have sex in the context of a whole person, a person whose life is shared with yours. The lover who has made love with you so passionately during the night is the same person beside you at dinner, concerned with your worries in your career, sharing your excitement at a new promotion. The person you had sex with that morning is the same person with whom you watch TV or plan a night on the town for dinner and disco dancing. Your lover is someone you know completely, whose humanity is both the springboard and shelter for your life. The sexual pleasuring you and your mate give each other is a magnetic reinforcement enhancing the depth of your commitment to each other, expressing the safety, security, and passion you share through the years.

As a couple, you are able to experience all the intensities of sexual feeling—the tender communication of making love, the passionate joy of lusting, and the physical release of sex. All arenas of sexual activity can be available to you; your mate has several sexual "selves" and moods. Monogamy can be as sexually thrilling as any sexual choice. And your sexual joinings within that monogamy are unique, forged out of the specialness each of you share as individuals. How you feel about sex is an expression of you. All sexual stances, all sexual wishes, are acceptable. You and your mate explore each other's sexual psyches, accepting, sharing, and knowing how you are similar and different. The two of you together define and decide the nature of your sexual relationship. Whatever you two do, whatever you feel, is okay. Your sexuality is part of you, an expression of you and your relationship, and as such is as whole, beautiful, and lovable as you are.

This is not to say that recreational sex is "bad," or that sampling a variety of partners is sinful. There are many exciting possibilities in our society. Certainly a long-term monogamous relationship is not morally, spiritually, or sexually superior to other life choices. Monogamy and sampling sexual spice through a variety of relationships are two different things. Each requires a different life-style, different relationships, different commitments. One is not "better" or more sexually or psychologically "advanced" than the other.

For too long, our society has dictated how to have sexual pleasure, has handed down rules and ideals that diminished freedom and choice. Women, for example, were first told that "ladies" should not experience sexual pleasure; later, orgasm became okay. Then even that was not enough—some had to have vaginal rather than clitoral orgasms. Now there is a sense that if you don't know where your G-spot is and are not able to orgasm for fifteen minutes, you are somehow sexually inadequate or not as sexually fulfilled as you could be. At first, men were taught that their sexual desires were so disgusting that they could not be enjoyed with a wife, but only with "fast women." Later, men had the pressure of being the sexual leader and teacher, responsible for pleasuring themselves and their partners. Now men are coping with the impact of women's liberation and the standards of "macho" sexual performance. It can become oppressive and take all the fun out of sex as you anxiously worry if you are measuring up.

This book makes no statement regarding the various sexual choices available. Long-term monogamy and a variety of sexual partners are both possible in our society. *Keep the Home Fires Burning* supports and values the freedom for each of you to choose the life-style best for you. It is the intention of this book, however, to explore the possibility of an intimate, long-term, monogamous relationship that remains sexually exciting.

For the long-term couple, a good sexual relationship is crucial, as Philip Blumstein and Pepper Schwartz discovered in their study entitled *American Couples*. Sexual frequency is decisive in determining the happiness of a sexual relationship. Couples who make love frequently—one time or more per week—are more likely to be satisfied with their sexual relationship and have happy marriages. Furthermore, in *Love, Sex, and Aging*, Edward Brecher reported that marital happiness was more strongly associated with enjoying sex with one's spouse *than with any other factor.*

This is truly an amazing fact! Experts have wondered over and over why sex is as crucial as it is to marital happiness. Some suggest that sexual satisfaction is primarily a reflection of the happiness in other aspects of the relationship. Others suggest that perhaps joyful sex itself generalizes to the total relationship. Making love is a way of being close and creates a psychic connection. This bond is unique to the marital relationship. Regardless of whether a good marital relationship creates a good sexual relationship, or great sex creates a sense of marital happiness, they seem to go together. Perhaps they feed each other. A close relationship may enhance sex, which makes the relationship even closer and more loving. Being able to talk well together and being satisfied sexually correlate with a happy marriage.

Notice that the important question is whether you are satisfied with your sexual relationship with your spouse. Satisfaction is not determined by trying a different position every night, having marathon sexual sessions, or experiencing simultaneous orgasms. In fact, you do not even need to be orgasmic as long as you are satisfied with the sexual relationship you share together. And each of you gets to define what constitutes a satisfying sexual relationship. For some of you the closeness and affection exchanged in sex is the important component; for others, the release through climax is the powerful magnet. The crucial part is for the two of you to feel sex is satisfying and enjoyable without comparisons to mythical couples.

Maintaining a good sexual relationship is one of the most important things you do for your total relationship. Sex for the long-term couple has its unique pleasures and problems. The continuation of a high sexual frequency through the years you are together indicates how much fun sex still is for you. And most of you—63 percent after ten years—are making love once a week. Even after the age of fifty, the majority of you have sex at least that often. You are constant sexual companions, able to supply each other with joy whenever you wish. You are sexually safe and familiar with each other; you have taught each other how to achieve maximum gratification. The sexual joy and ecstasy you give each other brings you closer, helps to maintain your intimacy, and creates a bond of pleasure. You can rely on this bond to give you both pleasure in times of stress, in times of difficulty.

Yet as a long-term couple, you may find frequency of sex decreasing. Often the very aspects that make sex between long-term lovers so easy—knowing how to quickly pleasure your partner and yourself—can also make it routine and ritualized. Thus, sex becomes having the most orgasms in the shortest possible time as you use your skill and past sexual experience to bring your partner and yourself efficiently to the peak of satisfaction. This is product-oriented sex rather than process-oriented sex (in which the focus is on sharing, exploring, and knowing as well as pleasuring). Do you feel you haven't the time to devote to leisurely lovemaking? Do you find yourself running out of exciting new things to do together and feel that you're in a sexual rut, repeating the same pattern over and over? Perhaps your children are interfering with your sexual life, making spontaneity and privacy impossible. You may feel that all the pressures of your life come before exploring the passion you can feel for each other.

Keep the Home Fires Burning helps you enjoy the special pleasures and deal with some of the unique problems in a long sexual relationship. It gives suggestions on how to keep the fires of your sexual relationship stoked and ready to burst into bright flames. It tells how you can enhance your sexual relationship and make sex a priority again. There are suggestions and instructions for new things you can try together. This book is a road map to help you continue on a long and exciting sexual journey. It speaks to sex within the context of coupleness. You, the couple, know "how" to make love and want to keep the energy flowing, the excitement growing, and the experience changing. It will help you enhance the variety within your sexual relationship rather than through various partners. You and your mate can continue to explore each other and your sexual potential instead of relying on tried and true sexual habits. Or if you do not wish to explore new activities, you may use this book to put those same activities in different and novel contexts.

Just as your sexual contact strengthens your total relationship, so the relationship between the two of you is the keystone of your sexual relationship. In order to have a joyful sexual relationship you must feel good about both your own sexuality and your mate. If you are open, loving, caring, and see each other as separate, special people, the sexual feeling will remain strong between you. This book will help the energy grow and flower.

However, if you are having problems in your relationship that impinge on your sexuality, this book will not speak directly to you. Perhaps you have, without realizing it, picked a mate who so resembles a parent that sex feel incestuous. Maybe you have fears of intimacy or see your mate as smothering, intrusive, or rejecting. Angers, buried and allowed to fester, may have eroded your loving feelings. All these relationship difficulties impair the free flow of sexual trust and exploration and can be dealt with by solving the relationship problems first.

Some of you may feel a restriction of passion; sex has lost its luster, its thrill. Lack of sexual passion has increasingly become a symptom of unhappiness. Our society's obsession with sex and the expectation of quantities of sexual ecstasy may have inhibited your sense of sexual adequacy, leaving you to feel vulnerable and inept. *Keep the Home Fires Burning* may respark those old flames by helping you to discover and accept your own unique sexuality. Your sexuality is *your* sexuality. It need not be—like income, or number of miles run per day—measured by others' supposed or imagined achievements. Passion may also be renewed by increased variety and exploration. If your lack of passion is the result, however, of an emotional conflict, depression, or a pervasive feeling of discomfort regarding sexuality, then these issues may first be resolved by counseling or psychotherapy. *Keep the Home Fires Burning* is a handbook for you, the couple who has a working relationship in which the flow of communication and sexuality exists. Some of the suggestions in this book will fit easily into your sexual relationship; others may be new thrills which you add to your sexual repertoire or novelties for a special occasion. Some suggestions you may find unsuitable for your tastes. Your decision about this is an expression of you and—as in all matters of taste—not to be disputed, but respected and honored. This book is written to meet the needs of many different couples with different sorts of sexual temperaments, fantasies, and curiosities. It does not deal with sadomasochism or using bodily wastes for sexual pleasure.

Keep the Home Fires Burning is for the long-term couple; it describes couples enjoying aspects of their sexual relationship and gives theoretical and how-to information. The case examples will help you to experience the suggestions with your emotions, while the theoretical and how-to information provides additional ideas for you to try. Although none of the patients I have seen in my years as a psychotherapist and marriage and family counselor are in this book, their concerns are. Many of the suggestions here have been helpful to the people I have seen in my practice. The case examples in this book are fictionalized portraits of the people and couples I have met. The couples in the book have all been given heterosexual names starting with the same initial to make it easier and avoid confusion for the reader. This is not to exclude homosexual couples, since the issues and solutions are similar for all long-term couples regardless of sexual orientation. In fact, I have used many of the suggestions in this book in my work with lesbian and gay couples.

There is an evolutionary aspect for sex within the context of being a long-term couple. Together you build a life, aware of the lives of your parents before you and of the interaction between their past and your present. As you have children, you cast a net of hope for the future. Your sexuality together has created a new life. Your personalities and couplehood together nurture that new human being for future worlds and possibilities. This universal reason for our sexual intensity is acutely present in the long-term couple. In fact, it is our ability to pair bond that makes possible the development of human culture. And our ability to be continually sexual with each other—rather than only during an estrus cycle like other mammals—is necessary for the establishment of that pair bond. Both male and female have evolved a variety of permanent sexual attractions. The human female is the only mammal to have prominent breasts even when not lactating, and the human male has the most conspicuous penis of any primate. The pair bond that our human ancestors formed enabled the long nurturing and education of children. Thus, our unique sexuality has made possible the pair bond and all of human culture.

Such commonality with all mankind in no way jeopardizes your uniqueness. You are unique—the life you create together will never come again—another evolutionary try. You are a pair of glorious mammals together changing and altering your own lives and the small world around you. *Keep the Home Fires Burning* speaks both to the evolutionary aspects of sexuality that male and female have always shared and to the modern aspects of sexuality made possible by science and technology.

In a recent TV movie, a woman on her fifteenth wedding anniversary imagines her life married to three different men. In her fantasy, each man brings a new satisfaction to romance. She realizes that she and her husband could incorporate the best of her fantasies about the other men. Yes, her husband could bring her breakfast in bed; they could dress up in sexual costumes; they could go to Las Vegas on a wild weekend together. And, most important, she could do all those things with her husband. This is the message of *Keep the Home Fires Burning.* Over a period of twenty or thirty years you can have as much variety and excitement as you like, exploring sexual adventures with your long-term mate. There is no need to jeopardize love, family, and security for an exciting adulterous affair. You can have an affair with your mate. Here's how.

1

SETTING THE STAGE

All day she thought about making love that night with Fred. All day, while chasing after two preschoolers. Now she seemed too exhausted to bother picking up their cluttered bedroom. Clothes piled on baskets were waiting to be folded at the foot of their unmade bed, the rumpled sheets were the same ten-year-old set her mother had given her before she went to college. "Well, I'll close my eyes and pretend I'm in a daisy-dotted field, and Fred and I can have a quicky. At least a few moments of pleasure after such a shitty day. But this has to change." And Frances resolved to create a more romantic atmosphere—one more conducive to making love.

You, too, may be unhappy with the place your sexual relationship has in your life. In the beginning, you and your lover could barely wait to be together, to steal off to a quiet place where you could leisurely and intensely explore each other's bodies, delve into each other's minds. Your sexual relationship seemed so precious then. New and novel, thrilling and blissful, each sensation, each caress brought forth heady feelings and knowledge. The two of you may have explored every position, every sexual act you had read about or imagined. All was new, all was exciting; you had made your sexual relationship the number-one priority.

But now sex may be farther down on your list of priorities—after making sure dinner is made and the living room is picked up, after watching the evening news, reading your son his new book, and quizzing your daughter on her spelling words. No longer new, no longer an adventure, sex may have become a quick, easy body rubbing at the end of the day.

Together as a couple you decide the emphasis of sex in the total picture of your relationship. For some of you, sex is an extremely important part of your life, an activity that you explore both quantitatively and qualitatively. It rings throughout your relationship as a theme, a way you share and are close. It feels like a crucial part of life to you, and a powerful sexual contact can make your whole world feel terrific. For others of you sex exists as background music—it is one of many ways to have pleasure together but is not a primary determinant of happiness. Each of these patterns and emphasis on sex is right. There is no "right" or "wrong" emphasis on sex, just as there is no ideal frequency of intercourse for everyone. It is your sexual relationship, and together you get to use it as you wish, making your own ideal place for sex in your life.

The emphasis you put on sex is not important, but the sexual relationship itself is. Immediately after I graduated from college, I was doing research on what makes a happy marriage. I was young and naive and hoped to find something terribly spiritual and romantic—like understanding and acceptance—which separated happy from unhappy marriages. What I found, over and over again, was sex. If you felt you had a good or terrific sexual relationship with your spouse, you were very likely to have a happy marriage. If you found sex with your spouse tolerable or disgusting, you were very likely to be unhappy and get a divorce. Sexual satisfaction was the single most important predictor of marital happiness. Everything else—common interests, similar background, time spent together—fell by the wayside in importance. Every poll since then has found the same thing.

This is not to say that in every single happy marriage there is a good sexual relationship or that everyone with a good sexual relationship has a happy marriage, but it sure helps get you through the rough spots. Sex is a form of sharing and communication, and it creates a powerful pleasure bond between you, holding you close when times get tough and guaranteeing ecstasy in the midst of chaos. Moreover, it is up to you to define your sexual relationship; you must decide how often is enough; you must decide what is fun. But regardless of the face of it, a mutually fulfilling sexual relationship is the cornerstone of your marriage.

In order to maintain your sexual relationship, you must sometime make sex a priority. For most of you, your lover and your sexual relationship were number one in the beginning. As the years passed, your life became crowded with commitments clamoring for your attention and sex may have receded in importance. For many of you sex will again take precedence once your children have left home. These fluctuations are part of the normal life couples share. They are to be expected and accepted, they are not necessarily a sign of either dwindling or increasing sexual interest. Sexual neutrality fluctuates with sexual passion. Periods of sexual quiescence provide the potential for renewal and intensity.

This is how it should be. Your sexual relationship cannot and should not always be your number-one priority. Rather, the predominance of your sexual relationship is going to ebb and flow throughout your life together. Sometimes, when you feel particularly passionate and the rest of your life is peaceful, sex will be near or at the top of your list of priorities, receiving months of extra attention and exploration. At these times, your sexual relationship may be rekindled and it will increase in passion. The bond of closeness between you is strengthened by this mutual pleasuring, forming a safety net for your relationship.

At other times, your sexual relationship may be lower on your list of priorities, crowded out by other concerns such as children, jobs, health, parents. At these times, your sexual relationship can be comfortable, easy, and satisfying. Now you call on the pleasure bond and use the understanding you have built during those times when sex was a priority. The knowledge of how to pleasure each other learned from the times of intensity is tested; you can quickly and easily satisfy each other, giving pleasure and reaffirming your love and closeness. A time of indifference makes possible a time of resurgence and rediscovery. There are many ways to reintensify your sexual relationship. Creating a romantic aura in your bedroom, devoting time to your sexual interludes, changing the locale of your lovemaking, and maintaining an attractive body are all ways to make your sexual life more important.

Making Sex a Priority

YOUR ROOM. Frances closed her eyes as Fred entered her, imagining herself sinking into a daisy-dotted field, the white-and-yellow flowers bobbing around her. But it did not work. Instead, she saw the laundry, which needed folding, and the worn striped sheets underneath her. She was having difficulty blotting out the reminders of tasks not accomplished. Her resolve to create a more sensual aura in their bedroom was strengthened.

The next day she straightened up the bedroom, making a place in the TV room for folding laundry. Frances remembered the day she and Fred made love in a field of wildflowers. Their bodies were hidden by the bobbing flower heads around them, and they felt transported into a private world together. It was one of their most terrific sexual times together. She somehow wanted to re-create the feeling of freedom they had when they were younger. She found some flowered sheets on sale. Frances gathered the ends and strung them up on the walls from floor to ceiling. Then she painted the trim a bright yellow and the ceiling a sky blue. Fred was thrilled with the changes. Their bedroom looked inviting, as though something important could take place there. The redecorated bedroom reminded Fred of that day in the meadow and how ardent their relationship was. He felt that Frances was eager for him and eager to make sex an exciting part ot their lives. He bought a bottle of champagne and a big bouquet of flowers to celebrate the daisy bedroom. Sex had been given a stage.

Perhaps, as it did with Frances, the condition of your bedroom reveals the priority you place on sex. Your bedroom may be the last room decorated; even your children's rooms are arranged for them—their toys, their books, their quiet times. Your bedroom is where you sleep, make love, and get dressed. It may be the only place where the two of you can be alone to talk or retreat from all your other roles. Your bedroom can be a place for just the two of you to be yourselves, to be man and woman together. It is your space.

Think about how you use your bedroom, and think about how you would like to use it. How you arrange it and decorate it can reflect how you use it. And regardless of how else you use it, it is probably the place where you most often make love. With a little time and imagination you can create an atmosphere that heightens sexuality.

Take a good look around your bedroom. Does it enhance or detract from your sexuality? First, get rid of the things that distract you sexually. Perhaps you have routinely kept the TV on during sex. Turn it off sometimes. You can't listen to TV and concentrate on the feelings between you and your lover. Maybe a table is piled high with work beckoning you—a reminder of something else to do which prevents you from focusing on sexuality. Move the table or screen it.

Second, you can add sensuality, after you have eliminated the unpleasant things. Environment can enhance your emotions by appealing to your sense of sight, smell, and touch. Close your eyes and imagine a place where you'd like to make love. Do you, like Frances, want to sink into a daisy-dotted field, or would the sun and sea, the blue sky of a beach, appeal to you? Would you like to be surrounded by the exciting colors of red and purple or the fresh greens of a forest? Imagine the place and try to duplicate it in your bedroom. Maybe you'd like to lie in an all-black bedroom, feeling cozy and secure together, with a window overlooking a vista of twinkling lights. Perhaps you'd like to create a party atmosphere, using bright colors and streamers to express a vibrant gaiety. Clearly, each mood reflects your sexual style and your sensual temper. Pick the colors and textures that appeal to your senses and add to your sense of sexuality.

Third, don't forget that your bed can enhance your theme and sensuality. What texture would seem sensual to you? Perhaps silky sheets would feel good against your skin, or maybe you would prefer the softness of flannel. Does lace somehow spark a feeling of luxurious sexuality in you, or are you excited by the drama of hiding away surrounded by a canopy and curtains? Mirrors on the wall may not only serve a function when you get dressed in the morning; you may find it exciting to watch yourselves make love, watching your lover move and feeling it at the same time.

Fourth, music may also add to the mood you are creating. Like Bo Derek in *10*, you may enjoy listening to a rhythmic beat as it builds to a crescendo. The pounding force of rock or the gentle soothing of classical music may suit the tempo of your sexual movements. Radio, tape player, or phonograph all add music and also serve to mask the sounds of sex from your child's ears.

YOUR BODY. Feeling good about your body is important for your sexual relationship. You don't have to be model thin or Stallone muscular to be sexy to others. In fact, it is not helpful to you or your lover to compare yourself to centerfolds, models, and athletes. Those expectations and standards can only serve to make you feel inadequate and to make your lover feel criticized. After all, few of us attain those standards of beauty. Rare, exquisite physical beauty does not guarantee happiness or a satisfying sexual relationship. We are human beings with blemishes, moles, cellulite, hair, and scars. Loving another means accepting the other as a human being, not comparing that person to an airbrushed ideal. Beyond initial attraction, feeling sexual is not determined by the body of your lover. Research done by Weight Watchers indicates that the excess poundage of its members does not turn off their spouses. However, those who feel they are overweight feel less sexual. Perhaps they are embarrassed by their bodies or feel they are unattractive.

Although you do not need to attempt to sculpt your body into the media ideal, sex is a physical act, and your body is your sexual equipment. It is important for you to be as attractive as you can be. You will feel that you are sexier and you will increase your erotic appeal for your partner if you maintain a fit and well-groomed appearance. Certainly you need to be in sufficient physical shape to be able to engage sexually. If you are so out of shape that you tire easily, exhaust yourself before you are finished sexually, then your sexual relationship will suffer. If you are in good physical shape, you will have increased your energy as well as your sexual abilities. Being physically fit can be a statement that your body and your sexuality are important to you. Those of you who are involved in sports reap the benefits in your increased physical and mental well-being and sexual stamina. However, recent findings indicate that there are outside limits to this. Excessive athletic endeavors decrease male sexual hormones and interrupt the woman's menstrual cycle. This may lower sexual interest and may decrease sexual frequency. The important thing about your body, then, is that you feel good about it, that you feel it is strong, healthy, and attractive.

TIME. For most of you, the crucial way to give priority to your sexual relationship is by making a special time for sex. Couples who make love frequently are more satisfied with their sexual relationship and feel more positive about each other. It is likely that couples who enjoy sex together make love more often. However, it seems that simply making love more often increases sexual satisfaction and positive feelings about the whole relationship. Perhaps if a couple does anything that is fun three times a week, they will be happier together than if they do it only once a month. It might also be that physical intimacy generalizes feelings of closeness throughout the entire relationship. Whatever the reason, research implies that simply increasing the frequency of sex enhances your satisfaction and marital happiness. Frequent sexual contact reinforces the pleasure bond, generalizing to the entire relationship. In spite of this, couples say they do not make love as often as they'd like because of lack of time. Devoting time to sex will increase the quality and quantity of your sexual relationship.

You need to spend time talking with each other about sex, dreaming up things to do or telling each other what has been good. You need this time when you are not exhausted from the day's work. Tiredness and tension are the foes of intense sex. You need time to slowly make love, prolonging the foreplay, moving to the slow, soft rhythms of intercourse. You need time to bask in the afterglow, cuddling, caressing, feeling that special closeness between two lovers whose bodies are spent. And you need time to rest before making love and sharing each other yet again.

Yet far too often, you allow the business of the day to crowd out sex. You may think, "I can make love anytime." Or, "Let's just have a quicky tonight, dear." You may honor time demands from all your other commitments; your children, your job, even volunteer work and repainting the house may take priority. It feels as if sex is always there, can easily be delayed or hurried, but these things must be done now! Your sexual relationship has again been swept under the rug, ignored, and treated callously. Of course, as stated above, your sexual relationship will not always be a priority. Sometimes it must and should be treated casually. But if that is your constant pattern, if you never give yourself the luxury of a whole evening to make love, your sexual relationship will not grow.

You both need to be relaxed to focus totally on the physical exchange between you. Perhaps you are a couple who would want to start a sexual evening together with dinner or a movie. Perhaps getting into bed and spending a few hours talking together acts as an aphrodisiac for you. Maybe taking turns giving each other sensual massages would provide a transition from the hassles of the day to the sensuality of a night making love. You can get in bed two or three hours early to make love.

Perhaps you will routinely schedule one evening a month or a week to devote to sex. Some of you may think that this decreases spontaneity or worry that you will feel you have to perform sexually. Yet so much else in your lives may be scheduled that unless you set aside an evening for a "sex date" with your mate, you will not have one. You do not have to have genital sex; it can simply be a time made sacred to spend together physically, enjoying each other's bodies. The rest of your sexual relationship can be as spontaneous as usual. Together as a couple you will discover what works for you. When you devote an entire evening to being sexual together, you are eloquently saying how important it is to you. You are making sex a priority, nurturing your relationship.

How often you spend time on sex is as individual as you are. Just as each couple decides how often to have sex, each couple also decides how long to spend being together sexually. Some of you may want to spend two or three evenings a week, for others one evening a month, or two or three very intense periods throughout the year. The important thing is that it is enough for you as a couple.

Calvin and Cynthia had just moved to a new city. Their children were with Calvin's parents so that they could set up the new house without being distracted by them. Although tired from the drive, they unloaded the rental truck. Boxes were piled high waiting to be unpacked, furniture was stacked haphazardly, waiting to be arranged. Calvin and Cynthia moved their mattress to their new bedroom, found sheets, pillows, and blankets, and fell exhausted into a deep sleep.

In the morning, they woke feeling disoriented in the new room. Cynthia cuddled close to Calvin, feeling his warmth and his erect penis. The ease of their bodies, the morning closeness, aroused them both and they made love. They lay in bed enjoying the rarity of a morning without parental duties, decided to delay the horrendous chores ahead of them, and made love again. They explored the neighborhood grocery, bought some food, came home, and made love yet again. They rested and talked, enjoyed the luxury of a nap in the middle of a day. They made love yet again, then unpacked a box or two so they could cook, and went back to bed where they made love again. They were doing the same old things sexually, but if felt different. Calvin and Cynthia's children were gone and they were free in a way they had not been for several years. They felt as if they were stealing time, not doing what they were "supposed" to be doing—almost as if they were kids just let out of school to play. They spent the entire four days in bed talking, exploring each other sexually, making love, and playing. The more times they made love, the more they wanted each other. It seemed as if years of mundane, routine sex had been swept away by the intense, terrific sex of those four days devoted only to each other. Cynthia felt they had not only rekindled the passion of their sexual relationship, but she also had discovered new things. Her orgasms were deeper and stronger than ever; her vagina was more sensitive and her orgastic response quicker. Calvin felt sexually sated and revitalized; they buoyantly arranged furniture in the new house, which their passionate sex had blessed with a marvelous omen. The feelings from those four days carried over into their lives. A period of indifference to sex was followed by a time of fervor. They made love more often, they enjoyed it more, they felt closer.

You as a couple will find your own way to devote time to your sexual relationship. Perhaps, like Cynthia and Calvin, you will steal some time from other duties; or perhaps you will need to schedule time. You can find your own hours, and places, your own devices. Together you may use time to make sex a priority. Together you assure that the time you set aside is made sacred by its importance in revitalizing and rekindling your sexual relationship.

Changing the Scenery

Just as spending more time on your sexual relationship can make it more exciting, so can changing the location. You don't even have to try to do new sexual things. Your favorite sexual routine takes on a different aura when performed in an unusual place or at an unusual time. So make love in a new place. Even a different room in your own house can add sexual excitement. Sometimes you can be swept away by the passion of the moment and make love on the kitchen table or the bedroom floor. The shower or bathtub offers a different place for sex as the slippery sensations of water and soap add variety to your sexual interlude. Hot tubs and Jacuzzis have increased in popularity not only to unwind and relax, but also as a way to be with your lover and explore the delights of underwater sex while you bask in the sensual feelings of warm, bubbling water. Adding food to your lovemaking and changing the time and place of contact can also revitalize your sexual relationship.

THE BED PICNIC. Roz knew just the kind of surprise Roger would love. She spent the whole morning shopping, picking up a good bottle of wine, smoked oysters, cheese, grapes, apples, and a loaf of French bread. All were foods she and Roger loved to eat on a beautiful summer picnic. Except it wasn't summer! It was the dead of winter and the snow hung thickly on the branches, the dampness chilling both of them to the core, the grayness sinking them into winter doldrums. Roz came home and turned up the thermostat, changed the sheets on the bed, put a musk bath oil on the light bulbs, and lit a few candles. The food was waiting, just enough to tantalize, not so much that they would feel stuffed. Looking around the room, Roz realized she had accomplished her goal and created a seductive atmosphere.

Roger came home tired and cold. The food was ready. He got in the bed already warmed by Roz's body, and they cuddled and talked about the day, warming up and feeling each other. He felt wanted and cared for, as if his needs had been anticipated; he had come home to a party for two. They made love. Roger poured a glass of wine and accidentally dripped some in the cleft between Roz's breasts. "We can't let that wine go to waste," he said, and bent over to lick it up, moving his tongue in between her breasts, making sure he lapped up every drop of the wine. He teased Roz, saying she made a terrific glass. She retaliated by saying he might, also, then laughed as she dribbled a little wine on his chest, letting it trickle down his abdomen. She traced her tongue down his chest, sucking up the little pool of liquid in his navel, teasing the hair at the top of his pubic area.

They then explored the possibilities of using each other's bodies as plates—Roger ate a grape out of her navel. Roz placed smoked oysters in a line down his body from his collarbone to the head of his penis and slowly ate the oysters one at a time. His growing erection moved the smoked oyster back onto his stomach. Roger placed a bunch of grapes over Roz's pubic area and nuzzled the plump fruits, lapping up the juice that trickled in her labia. Their wine-pouring, licking, and food-eating became more and more arousing, and soon they forgot the food, the wine, and their play and made love. Later, they lay in bed warm and moist, feeding each other the rest of the smoked oysters, peeling the grapes and popping them into each other's mouths, sharing the apple. They had used food playfully and erotically. Wintertime picnics in bed, they decided, beat the summertime food fests in the park.

Like Roz and Roger, you can combine food and sex in two different ways during your bed picnic. You can use the food as you would during a standard picnic. A bed picnic creates the atmosphere of a romantic meal in the privacy and comfort of your own bedroom. Food has long been an appetizer for sex. Eating fulfills a basic need, a primal oral satisfaction. Eating with a lover allows you to share and enjoy both the taste of food and intimate talk. You can rest together after sex, then feed each other. Food can be another way of giving to each other, of satisfying a sensual physical need. This helps to create an aura of trust, of intimacy, and implies that other needs will be met, other sensual feelings satisfied.

Food can also be used as part of your sex play. Food has a sensual appeal in its taste and appearance. Fruit particularly resembles the sexual organs. The phallic elongation of a banana, the curving flesh around the seeded hole of a cut melon, the rounding cheeks of a peach, the triangular curls of a bunch of grapes—all recall the sexual organs. Like the sexual organs, fruit has its own unique taste and smell, fresh and ripe. In addition to appearing similar to the sexual organs, the act of eating can be sensual. This is when you imagine that what your lover is doing to the food can be what your lover does to you. When you see your lover suck and lap the flesh of a melon, you cam imagine his mouth on your labia, when you see your lover put a banana in her mouth, you can imagine her lips surrounding your penis.

Food can be used as part of your sexual act. You can go to the supermarket and browse through the produce section with an erotic eye. Pick vegetables and fruits that you can use sexually. Perhaps you'd like to eat a zucchini out of your lover's vagina, place pineapple rings on your lover's penis. Maybe you'd like to cover your lover's penis with chocolate syrup or dribble honey on your lover's breasts and slowly lick it off. You may wish to spray designs with whipped cream and then lap them up. Oils massaged onto the skin can help your bodies slide into new positions and glide together as you move. Juices can add lubrication as well as organic edible delights. Let your imagination soar, discovering a combination of your own unique foods and sexual tastes. Combining food and sex enhances the sexual element of the food and the playful intensity of the sex.

AFTERNOON DELIGHT. Harold knew his wife, Heidi, loved making love in the afternoon. That was when she felt most sexual, alive. It was the best time of day for her. Yet they never seemed to have the afternoon available anymore—they both worked during the week and on the weekend the children were always around. She had a vacation day coming, and Harold decided to take a "mental health" day and call in sick. He worked extra hard so that he would not feel he was neglecting his job, then went to a card store and bought seven cards, each one preparing her for a surprise on her vacation day. The cards all hinted at a thrill from a "secret admirer," and, as in a treasure hunt, the last card asked her to meet her "secret admirer" at a certain hotel in a specific room for her surprise.

Heidi, meanwhile, had a pretty good idea that her secret admirer was her husband. She bought new underwear for the occasion and got all dressed up for her surprise. Excitedly, she went to the hotel, feeling as if she were on an illicit errand as she took the elevator to the room. Harold had a bottle of wine waiting. He kissed her and took her to bed, where they spent the afternoon being together and making love. At three-thirty Heidi left so that she would be home when the children arrived from school. Later, when Harold came home for the family dinner, he winked at her. Chuckling over their secret afternoon, they pretended it had been just another ordinary day. The contrast between the stolen "illicit" afternoon and the nightly family routine made the memory even more delicious and exciting. Throughout their years together Heidi and Harold would occasionally sneak off to make love in a hotel.

Afternoon delight with your spouse can have all the elements of an illicit affair. You can arrange to meet in a hotel, discovering at the desk which room your spouse has reserved. Or you can "play hooky" from work and start with lunch, then go to a hotel or go home. In other words, you can arrange it as you would an extramarital affair. Or, if your work schedules permit, you can set aside a time on a regular basis to be together. It does not have to be in the afternoon, a late leisurely morning in bed during the week can feel like the ultimate in luxury. You may decide to spend your afternoon at a movie matinee or taking a walk together. It is amazing how exciting simply being together on a weekday can be. It feels out of the ordinary, something different from your usual schedule, and in changing the time you make love you are adding variety to your sexual relationship.

THE WEEKEND SHACK-UP. Even more intense than afternoon delight can be a weekend shack-up with your spouse. You would need to arrange child care for your children and then go to a hotel together. Don't pick an exciting place: you might be tempted to spend time sight-seeing. A neighboring town even more boring than your own would be a good place. Obviously, going to a famous ski resort at the height of the ski season if you are both avid skiers is not conducive to spending intense time with each other. One of those hotels with a swimming pool, sauna, and whirlpool may add to your sensual experience. Some cities have steambaths with swimming pool, food, and massages which they open to couples one evening a week. Or you may find a spot out in the country if time spent outdoors brings you closer.

There are also X-rated motels which offer specific sensual delights for a couple. Some offer XXX-rated movies on their TV, or water beds, or massages. You may want to try this out sometime. The purpose of the weekend shack-up is to revitalize your sexual relationship by getting away from the demands of your regular life, away from the pressures of your jobs, the demands of your children, the interruption of the telephone, and the distraction of the TV—to be alone together so that you can devote time to each other.

THE VACATION. It seemed like it had been years since they were alone together. Mary and Mark were eager for this trip to Mexico—nothing to do but lie in the sun and snorkle, explore the old Mayan ruins. Eat. Make love. Walk together, talk together. With a mixture of guilt and relief, they sent the kids off to camp. As they saw their children leave, Mark said, "Alone at last. . . . No more parenthood for a full month. Yipppee!" They were excited about their vacation, and yet each felt a gnawing concern—they had not been alone together for any length of time during the last twelve years. What if they didn't get along as well as they used to or found little to do together? What if all they had in common were the kids, their house, and their friends? Still, they felt like two kids let out to play, like newlyweds embarking on a honeymoon.

Their vacation turned out to be even better than they'd dreamed.

At first they were so exhausted from their hectic city lives and the extra hassle of getting their children packed for camp that they sat speechless, staring into the lapping waves. Mary wondered when they were going to have a meaningful talk. But the sea had a soothing effect and they were able to come close together, to open up again to each other, to talk again of their dreams and fears, the basic elements that had brought them close together in the beginning. They disco-danced till dawn, arousing each other with body motions that mimicked intercourse—slowly grinding, quickly rubbing, to a crescendo of motions—then they held each other close as they swayed through a slow ballad. They spent hours walking on the beach, holding hands, watching their legs move to the same pace, stopping to pick up a shell, and feeling the waves lap at their ankles. Snorkling to see the wonders of the rainbow-colored fish and the world beneath the sea became a new hobby for them. They used the intimate physical knowledge they had of each other and worked as a team. Underwater, as above water, they relied on each other; they pointed out thrilling sights, moved together almost as one. The underwater world was a sensual experience; the slowly undulating sea ferns and the waving fish showed them new visual delights. The feeling of the water and sun, the sound of the air sucking through their mouthpieces, and the new signals they used created for each a different awareness of the other.

All these new tempos, new smells, and new sounds were reflected in their sexual joinings. Sex was a part of every day. They made love when they chose, using the wondrous new scenery as a prelude for their bodies touching. Slowly they savored each other, spending an entire day stroking each other's bodies, each teasing the other. They brought each other to the point of orgasm and then relaxed to rearouse themselves again. One night they made love in the sea, the slow music of the waves setting the rhythm for their own sexual motions, the buoyancy of the salt water carrying them along. Later they tasted the salt water on each other's bodies, the primal salt taste reminding them of sexual fluids. Their favorite day was their simplest. They had done nothing except snorkle outside their hotel and spend the afternoon in bed making love, napping and eating dinner to make love again that evening. They returned home refreshed, having rekindled their relationship—both emotionally and sexually.

A vacation in a romantic spot, alone, is the ultimate change in location and time, allowing you to be together. Tension and fatigue are cast aside. The sight-seeing and scenery are shared experiences. As you explore a new world, you are stimulated to reexplore each other, to be reminded of the wonderful qualities of your lover as you see them again in a new place without the distractions of your day-to-day lives together. Again you are reminded of why you fell in love, and you see the growth and confidence that years of living together have stimulated.

By spending time together, by changing the location of your sexual interludes, and by supplying a romantic aura, you are reaffirming the priority of your relationship, your shared sexuality. This reaffirmation, this strong statement of the importance of your lover to you, rekindles your relationship. Without changing the sexual content of your joinings you have increased the sexual intensity—the oneness, the fusion of your lovemaking. You can realize how much you cherish each other. You may feel that if you are stranded on an island, you would choose to be with your spouse.

2

THE SENSUAL, SEXUAL SELF

Ben had always enjoyed sex, and he especially loved it with Barbara, his wife. He gently stroked her, sensitive to the nuances of her responsiveness, aware of the hardening of her nipples, the moistening of her labia, and the arching of her back. Empathizing with her delight, he felt his own sexual power through the quickening of his breath, the pulsating of the blood to his penis. His body sang with the motions of intercourse. It was so great Ben wanted more. He wished he could make love again and again that night, and he knew Barbara would open up for him. Although he felt spent, as if much of his energy had been sapped, he could feel the undercurrent of more desire. He wanted to challenge his sexual athleticism. He decided the promise of pleasure and the enlarging of his sexual horizon were worth the risk. Ben placed Barbara's hand on his penis and moved closer to her. She seemed surprised at his continued interest, as they had seldom made love more than once on each occasion. "It was so terrific, I want an encore," Ben whispered.

Ben moved his head between her legs, sucking on the head of her clitoris. Her excitement rose quickly, she was like a pump already primed, it was easier for her to spurt her fluids a second time. Again his penis was hard and throbbing, and he entered her. She came quickly, and Ben enjoyed the feeling of her warmth surrounding and containing his penis, of her vaginal muscles as they contracted, caressing his penis from within. Then he spurted inside her and felt his body relax.

"Boy, I guess love is better the second time around," Ben said. "We have to try that more often. I wasn't sure I was up to it. Ha-ha! Did you hear my joke?"

"Yeah. You must be tired now. I always knew you could. If you think you can, you can," said Barbara sleepily as she snuggled her head on Ben's shoulder.

Developing a Positive Self-Fulfilling Prophecy

Barbara's comment is very accurate. Your sexual capabilities take place primarily in your head. In fact, three things determine sexual desire: heredity, the level of the hormone testosterone, and your state of mind. The importance of heredity in sexuality is difficult to determine. There are some indications that biological factors play a part. For example, in women there is a correlation between age of onset of menses and orgasmic capacities; apparently, women who start menstruating very late are less orgasmic.

However, your state of mind affects the levels of sexual hormones in your body, so you can see the importance of your feelings and attitudes toward your sexual desires and possibilities. The number of times you can make love and the number of times you can have an orgasm are largely determined by your motivation and the attitudes you have about sex and your sexual fitness. If you assume you can make love three or even eight times in one day, you may be able to. If you assume that you can only make love once a week, you will only be able to make love once a week. I remember meeting John, a married medical student, who informed me that men could only make love one time a week. He was certain that making love more often than that would sap so much energy that no male could accomplish anything else. That may have been true for this particular man. Clearly, since he believed it to be true, it probably was his sexual horizon. He could conceive of no greater frequency of sex. I hope, however, that before he began practicing medicine he became further educated on the subject, since many men make love more frequently than one time a week.

At the other end of the continuum, I met a man for whom making love eight times a day with a new lover was his response to an exciting new partner. Such a performance was an indication to him of sexual attraction between the two people and not an Olympian feat. Woody Allen has a marvelous scene in *Annie Hall* which addresses the individual assumptions we all have regarding sexual frequency. The man is talking with his psychiatrist, complaining that his lover *never* wants to make love—that he is forced to go around horny all the time. They are only making love three times a week. Simultaneously, the woman partner is talking with her psychiatrist, complaining that her lover *always* wants to make love and is constantly hounding her for sex. All this pressure, even though they make love three times a week! Clearly, each of us has a different "thermostat" of sexual desire and frequency. And like the thermostat in your house, your sexual horizon can be lowered or raised. If you want to change your sexual performance assumptions, you must undertake a two-part task. The first and most important part takes place in your head. If you think you can, you can. If you think you cannot, you cannot. Sexual performance is a perfect example of a self-fulfilling prophecy. Second, your body must be able to respond. If you're tired, have been drinking too much, or are physically unfit, you will be less able sexually.

There are sexual exercises that enhance orgasmic capabilities. And as with everything else sexual, each of you gets to decide if you want to change your sexual horizon. Many of you will be very happy with your present sexual frequency. You may feel that spending thirty minutes a day practicing vaginal exercises will overburden your already busy schedule. In addition, you may have no wish to train for a more athletic sexual performance, sex may not be important to you in that way. You may enjoy your orgasms as they are or enjoy sex without orgasm. Others of you will want to increase your sexual interest, or the number of times you can orgasm, or the strength of your orgasm. Perhaps your partner would like to make love more often, or perhaps you would like your orgasms to be more powerful. This chapter discusses how to raise your sexual thermostat.

IF YOU THINK YOU CAN, YOU CAN. The first step in changing your sexual performance is in thinking you can do it. But you can't talk yourself into it as if you were bolstering your confidence. You must define yourself as a sexual person, owning and allowing your sexuality. It is by feeling good about your own sexuality, by feeling free to express your sexual feelings, that you increase your sexual performance.

There is a paradox when it comes to sexuality and sexual performance. Because so much of your sexual responses are involuntary and not under the control of your conscious mind, you cannot make a decision regarding your performance and simply expect your body to perform. In fact, the more you want it, the more elusive it may become. Your insistence on orgasms or an erection may make you so tense that you drive your sexual feelings away. If, for example, you decide, "This is the night I'm going to make love four times," your unconscious may play a trick on you. Your body picks up on any unconscious anxiety you may have and can react with a shutdown of sexual responsiveness.

Let's go back to John, the medical student who was convinced that he could make love only once a week. Let's suppose that a friend tells him that he makes love twice in one day. John then decides that this is the night he is going to do it. He is going to perform as well as his friend! He will make love twice that night! His unconscious hears the fear underneath the bravado. Maybe he is not as good as his friend. Maybe he can't do it two times. Maybe once a week really is his limit. That night, after a perfectly delightful sexual interlude with his wife, his anxiety mounts. He doesn't feel sexual, just turned off. Maybe he'll not be able to get another erection. Then, of course, since sex is the perfect self-fulfilling prophecy, he can't. John's attitude that sex once a week is all that is possible is thus reinforced, but in addition he feels somehow inadequate and cheated.

On the other hand, John could have a different experience. Suppose he reads that many couples make love three or four times a week. John reacts with, "Ah, maybe I was wrong, maybe men can have sex more than once a week. I think I'll try it sometime." Two days after he and his wife have made love, John finds himself thinking about sex. Ordinarily he would have ignored those feelings, but this time he makes a sexual overture to his wife. She responds and the two of them happily make love. John has changed his attitude about sex.

What is the way out of this dilemma, then? If you can't simply decide to change your sexual expectations, then how do you change your performance? If sexual performance is largely a self-fulfilling prophecy based on unconscious attitudes and feelings, then how do you alter the prophecy to change the performance? You can't hit it head on and expect a change, since your arousal, orgasm, and rearousal arise as an automatic, involuntary response to a set of physical and psychical feelings. But you can increase your sexual performance by going at it "sideways," so to speak, by getting everything ready—your mind and your body—and allowing it to happen. You concentrate on your feelings, sensing the buildup of even more powerful sensations.

Perhaps the best analogy is the "let-down" reflex when you are breast-feeding. This is when your milk flows into your breast from deep within the chest wall to spurt into your baby's mouth. It is accompanied by a very definite prickly feeling in your nipple. The let-down is a conditioned response, out of your conscious control—a reaction to a set of physical stimuli, such as your baby crying or the pressure of full milk in your breasts. Additionally it can be stimulated by a set of emotional stimuli or images, such as knowing the pleasure of the flowing milk, unhook your bra as you settle into your usual rocking chair, feeling any warm, cozy feeling. All these can start the milk flowing. Like orgasm, the let-down reflex can be stopped by tension, worry about the amount of milk you have, or physical pain.

Your body has learned to respond to sexual stimuli in certain ways. Perhaps your lover's erect penis or the images of your wife's vulva waiting for you to enter are erotic to you. These stimuli can be used to maintain or increase arousal. Improving your sexual performance comes when there are no impediments, when you are physically and emotionally enjoying being a sexual person.

You know you are sexual and you concentrate on enjoying what you are doing with your lover. You can set it up so you delve into your own erotic events. Have your lover tickle you with her hair, dive into the delicious aromas from her genitals. Imagine and remember the two of you exchanging your sexual fluids, the warm and powerful feeling you will have. All these pieces make up your sexuality. As you respond to them they become even more imbued with erotic power, are thus even more potent in arousing you. You have a rich erotic network which you can rely on. Feeling and concentrating on the pleasure you are exchanging with your lover and your own physical and emotional sensations increase your sexual performance. So that if you think you can, you can.

ALLOWING AND OWNING YOUR SEXUALITY. Developing a positive self-fulfilling prophecy for your own sexuality is dependent on your definition of yourself as a sexual person. We are sexual beings at birth. Responding with sexual feelings to certain touches, certain sights, certain smells, and certain sounds is part of the equipment you came with. Allowing sexuality and sensuality is how sexuality starts. When you were a baby you allowed your mother to please you, you responded to her caring for you with pleasure. She fed you, you blissfully sucked, feeling relaxed, at one with the world. She massaged your little body with oil, and the nerves on your flesh responded, feeling her feeling you.

As an adult, you *allow* yourself to have feelings of sensuality and sexuality. You may enjoy being passive while your lover pleases you. You hand your sexuality over to her, letting her decide what and when and how you will be pleased. You may be aroused by the gentle touch of her fingertips on your palm, by the smell of your lover's armpit, or by the sound of his voice vibrating across the headboard of your bed as you both lean against it talking. The sight of your lover's bare breasts or erect penis may be exciting to you. All the world is open for your sensual enjoyment. You passively allow the sensual and sexual feelings in, letting yourself enjoy the sensations.

Owning your sexuality is the active part of this duo. You are sexual, you are sensual, and you are responsible for the pleasure you experience. You may give yourself sensual experiences. Perhaps your body tingles with delight at the mere thought of a sauna and massage with fragrant lotion. You may make requests of your lover, asking him to kiss you longer, asking her to sit astraddle you for a while. You recognize that the pleasure is *yours*, it is for *you*! Sexual pleasure is an end in itself, it is not only to please your lover, to impress each other with your prowess, beauty, or passion. It is a good feeling that you can have, that you can give. In owning your sexuality, you accept the responsibility for your pleasure. Your lover does not *make* you come; you do it.

These two aspects of sexuality—allowing and owning sexual and sensual pleasure—are crucial for a rich, full sexual life. Sexual awareness, being able to relax your body, a positive attitude toward your body, knowing when your body is sending signals of arousal—all are necessary steps for you to be able to respond sexually. In allowing sensual and sexual pleasure, your body is ready to experience the physical world in all its glory—the smell, taste, touch of life itself. You can delight in and respond to all the possible beauties and feelings from your lover's body. And by owning your own pleasure you can make sure that your body will have the chance to respond to its most exciting, fulfilling activities. You and your lover will be able to give and get, each of you together. You can switch roles, perhaps one being passive and receiving, then being active and giving. You are able to experience the challenges and joy of both requesting and fulfilling.

HOW TO ALLOW SEXUALITY

1. GIVE YOURSELF PERMISSION. Maybe you are one of the lucky ones and your mother enjoyed giving you pleasure. She loved making you feel good, seeing you snuggle in bed after a warm bath, rocked and sung to until you felt in harmony with the world. She did not recoil with horror when you grabbed at your genitals when the air hit them while she diapered you. Your father did not smack your hand away or flinch when he saw you masturbating. They accepted that it was nice for you to feel good and that someday you

would experience the greatest of all physical pleasures—sex and orgasm. They accepted your sexuality and thus gave you permission to feel good, being there to help you with information along the way. Unfortunately, such enlightened parents were a rarity in older generations and, because of the attitudes that most of us have incorporated, are still hard to find. So you may have some work to do before you can truly allow and own your sexuality.

You may have to give yourself permission to feel good. You do this by examining your own attitudes toward physical pleasure and freeing yourself from the incorporation of your parents' attitudes. You are a different person and do not have to be like them in all respects. The sexual renaissance that has taken place in this country over the last twenty years may have helped you feel more comfortable with your sexual feelings. It may have helped counteract any negative messages about sex that your parents had as a result of their cultural milieu. You realize that you do deserve to feel good, that your body is equipped with nerve endings to signal joy as well as pain, that physical and sexual pleasure are special, important parts of your life which you have the right to experience.

2. KNOW WHAT AROUSAL IS. Increasing your sexual awareness involves becoming attuned to the sexual feelings inside you, more aware of the sexuality flowing between you and other people, more aware of your sexual responses. Research was done recently on women's responses to watching pornography. The women reported that the erotic movies did not arouse them. However, physical data taken during and after the movie indicated that many were aroused. Perhaps you, too, may be unaware of the sexual clues from your body; perhaps you deny your sexual feelings. Women particularly may have this difficulty. Men have a clear signal—erection—which is evidence of their arousal.

Yet for women, too, there are specific signals that indicate arousal. You may have some or all of these. The physical signs of arousal are erect nipples, increased heart rate and breathing, a feeling of hotness in your vulva, erect clitoris, lubrication. Which of these are true for you? What is the first sign that you are turned on? Is it that tingly, hot feeling in your vulva or an itchiness around your clitoris that makes you want to rub? Or are you aware of wanting your nipples sucked as they get hard? These are the signs of your arousal. Spend some time experiencing them so that when you are aroused you know it. Then, when you feel that familiar sensation, you will correctly define it as arousal.

You may repress your sexual feelings because the behavior seems inappropriate for that time or place, or, like the women watching the movie, because you are embarrassed by what is making you feel sexual. You are not always able to act on your sexual feelings, but that doesn't mean they should be ignored, repressed, or sublimated. Let them flower and bloom, increase. Accept that they are *your* feelings regardless of whether or not you decide to act on them.

You need also to feel comfortable with your own body. Get familiar with your genitalia. Draw a picture of how you imagine them to look and then use a mirror to see how accurate you are. Learn how your muscles feel when they are tense and how they feel when they are relaxed. Practice slow, even breathing, feeling ease and peace spread throughout your body. Perhaps you can even imagine breathing in and out through your vagina.

3. KNOW WHAT SENSATIONS FEEL GOOD. Get in touch with the sensual pleasures possible for your body. Too often you may rush around attending to tasks, ignoring the glories surrounding you. You can concentrate on one sense at a time, spend a few days on each one of your five senses. Be aware of the world as experienced by that sense; take the time to enjoy and realize the fulfillment of that sense. For example, spend Monday and Tuesday on smell. Remember when you were a child and you learned the aromas of each object? You were even aware that each of your friends' homes had its unique aroma. Take the time to smell the odor of bread baking, the wind on a clear, crisp day, your own genital aromas. When you have refound your sense of smell, move on to another sense.

Listen to the rhythms of your dryer as it revolves, the purring of your kitten, or the rustle of the leaves in the trees. Many times you may have eaten almost mechanically, your mind on your conversation, the evening news, your job. Taste and smell your food, the texture of it, the sweet, acrid, or pungent taste of it. Then you can reexplore the world of touch and textures, rediscovering the cool smoothness of a stone, the velvety softness of fur, the scratchy feeling of sandpaper . . . and, of course, the nerve endings on your own skin. Appreciate the slide of silky fabric against your body; feel your hands feeling your flesh, and your flesh feeling your hands, as you smooth lotion or splash astringent on your body. By doing this, you can heighten your own responsiveness to feelings, sharpen each of your senses so your experience of the physical world is heightened.

Experiment with what touches are arousing to you. You already know what being turned on feels like. Be aware. Let yourself enjoy your erotic sensations. Masturbation is one way to learn exactly what touches, where and how, are most exciting for you. Touch yourself with light, feathery strokes so you can hardly feel your fingers. Blow on your skin. Now try touching harder, rubbing and moving rapidly. You can experiment on yourself and learn what rhythms, what postures, what degree of pressure is most erotic for you.

And don't forget that visual sights are also erotic. You men may be particularly excited by the sight of a beautiful woman's body, a bare breast or peach-shaped buttocks. Women, too, are excited by the visual. Learn what sights are arousing to you—perhaps it's the muscles in a man's legs flexing as he runs, a ballet dancer leaping in his tights. Maybe when your husband takes off his shirt you find your breath quickening.

4. TRUST SOMEONE TO PLEASURE YOU. Ben was thrilled with his new ability to make love two times a night. He began to think that there was more to the world of sexual pleasure than he had known. Like many men, he had no difficulty owning his sexuality; he knew what he liked sexually and felt little discomfort in taking the initiative, orchestrating his and Barbara's sexual music. For Christmas that year, Barbara decided to give him an hour-long full body massage. She had been taking classes in massage at the nearby YMCA during her lunch hour, so her new skill would be a complete surprise to him.

That night, as he undressed for his massage, Ben felt a feeling of vague apprehension. As he lay there not expected to do anything, he felt vulnerable, exposed. This was different from his accustomed role, his usual experience; he simply had to lay there receiving sensual pleasure. There were no performance demands, and he was not directing the events. Yet Barbara's palms pressing on his flesh felt good, her stroking and rubbing was soothing. He felt his tension dissolve under her touch, his feelings of vulnerability ebb away, and he relaxed, giving himself over to her for the experience. The scent from the lotion she was using echoed in his memory. . . . "Almonds," he thought, and remembered the milky lotion his mother used to rub on his face in the cold of winter. He became conscious of the smoothness of the sheet under his body and his skin prickled to alertness under Barbara's now soft touch as she smoothed his body with a soft furry material.

Ben felt totally at peace, as if all the corners of his body and his soul had been smoothed out. Relaxed. He realized he had had a new experience. He had turned himself over to Barbara, trusting her completely to give him pleasure, not controlling, but accepting, allowing. And it was a new kind of pleasure. It was not sexual pleasure, but sensual pleasure, and his sense of smell, the very nerve endings of his skin, seemed to have been reawakened. Ben had known how to own his sexuality; he had just had a lesson in allowing his sensuality.

Trust is the last step in allowing sexuality. You must trust that your partner wishes to please you. You accept that your lover is not a perfect mind reader, able to satisfy unspoken whims. But you know that he is well meaning. You know that your wishes are important to her. You are able to allow another person to please you.

HOW TO OWN SEXUALITY

1. REALIZE IT IS YOURS. This is the first step in taking responsibility for your own sexuality. By now, you know that you are a sexual person, you know what it feels like to be aroused, and you know what arouses you. Owning your sexuality is dependent on this. You also must be aware that no one else "makes" you climax, you do it. An orgasm usually requires both the physical stroking necessary and the fantasies and thoughts inside your head. No matter how fabulous your lover is, if your mind is on the stock market,

you won't climax. Additionally, you decide how, when, and with whom you are going to be sexual. You get to say no to events that are distasteful and seek out events that are exciting to you.

2. USE FANTASIES AND THOUGHTS TO HEIGHTEN YOUR AROUSAL. Remember the let-down reflex? The nursing mother conditions herself to let down by following a nursing routine, by imagining the milk squirting into her baby's mouth, by anticipating the warm feelings flowing between them. Sex is also a conditioned, involuntary response. You can use images to provoke a sexual response. Become aware of what images and fantasies turn you on. Use each of your five senses to alert you to sexual stimuli. Maybe it's the sight of your wife's breasts, the feel of her hair brushing against your shoulder, the smell of her genitals, the taste of her slightly salty flesh. Perhaps you imagine yourself a tower on which she is impaled, or you see her as a cave which you slowly enter and fill with light. You can imagine all these while you are preparing to make love.

Suppose you are washing dishes and a sexual thought crosses your mind. Ordinarily you would mentally toss it aside and concentrate on the task at hand. Don't. Instead, let the sexual thought grow and develop; perhaps you will journey down a path of sexual plans for that evening, becoming aroused as you imagine your wife making love to you. You can rehearse in your mind the sexual events for that evening. Perhaps you will find yourself embroidering a favorite sexual fantasy, feeling the arousal in your groin.

Now you can use these fantasies purposefully. Perhaps you and your mate have a "sex date" scheduled. A baby-sitter is hired and you have made reservations at a hotel. The atmosphere is set for romance. During the day, you can remind yourself to imagine your favorite fantasies; you can picture your most arousing images. You can feel the images working, as your arousal is evident to you. Your excitement and eagerness to see your mate build. When you both meet, your passion is evident, your arousal already guaranteed.

You also use fantasies during the sex act itself. These may involve thoughts of love about the person or seeing a specific body part that is erotic to you. Maybe you always imagine rockets exploding right before climax. Perhaps you replay a particular lovemaking session that was especially meaningful to you. Some of these thoughts may be so fleeting that you are not aware you even have them. You may use other fantasies to heighten your arousal or to time your climax so your sexual pace marches with your partner's.

3. ASK FOR IT. The last step in allowing and owning sexual pleasure is to ask for it. You and your lover have probably spent much time exploring yourselves and each other sexually. You know what you enjoy, you know where you like to be touched and how. Yet you may feel it is unfeminine or demanding to ask for what you would like. You may feel that your lover should automatically know what you want. Yet each of you would like nothing more than to please yourselves and each other. And neither of you is perfect at reading minds.

You can use nonverbal means to let your lover know what you want. You can move your lover's hand to the place you wish to be touched. Perhaps you would like your partner to touch you with more pressure. Put your hand on top of your lover's and press it with the degree of firmness you want. When your lover's touch is too firm, softly stroke her hand. If you wish your lover to move faster or slower, stroke your lover with the rate of motion you want at the time. For example, if your lover is moving his hand too quickly on your clitoris, rub his arm slowly. If you want your lover to know how excited you are, a firm squeeze communicates this. Twisting your spouse's penis by gently moving your hands in opposite directions on the shaft may be your signal that you are ready for intercourse. These hand signals communicate to your partner what would be most arousing to you at that time.

Sometimes you must ask for it in words. Far too often people balk at this stage. Actually putting a sexual request in words may be frightening to you. You may feel that you lack the courage. Certainly how you approach such a risk will depend on your daring as seen in other parts of life. But remember, you only have one life, and this is your spouse, your one chance to try what you want. This is where couple communication as well as your confidence in owning your sexuality is proven. For it is only when you ask for what you want that you can guarantee yourself the utmost in sexual pleasure. In the next chapter, there is a discussion on when, where, and how to ask for a sexual delight. Later on in the book, there are games that may also make this step easier for you.

For now, you need to have an "all systems go" approach to this final step in owning your sexuality; and you need to feel comfortable with the words you use. These can be slang words, scientific terms, or private codes you and your lover have evolved. But you need to have a vocabulary with which you are at ease. You may wish to repeat the words over in your own mind or write them down until "penis" and "vagina" are as familiar and easy for you to say as "apple" or "hand." And you need to know you have the right to ask. When you are comfortable with this last step you truly own your own sexuality. You have the psychological foundations for a rich sexual relationship.

By allowing and owning your sexuality and sensuality you have taken a huge step in developing a positive self-fulfilling prophecy. You are able to feel and enjoy your feelings. You can enjoy them for what they are; they are ends in themselves, there for you to enjoy regardless of whether you also have an orgasm. There is no rule that says sexual contact must end with orgasm or ejaculation. The sensation you experience and share with your lover can be enough. The closeness, excitement, and feeling of your penis contained by your lover's warmth or the rocking motions as you move together can be enough. It is your own feelings that are important, and appreciating and accepting your sensations and your lover's body is the essence for couples in allowing and owning their sexuality separately and together.

Sexual Athleticism

Now that you feel comfortable with owning your sexuality, you may wish to tune it up and train it a little. It is yours and you can change it, if you wish. You may want to increase how often you have sex. You may wish to increase the strength or frequency of your orgasms.

Take your sexual progress slowly. Walk before you run. Sex, like any athletic event, is built on prior experience and performance. Later on in this chapter, you will learn how to train yourself sexually. Only attempt to do one thing more at a time. Even if you feel like you can make love two extra times that night, keep yourself reined in and just try for one. You'll always get to try more the next time. You have a lifetime to explore each other.

HOW IT WORKS: THE BIOLOGY OF SEX. All the knowledge that science has amassed about sexuality can be used to develop realistic expectations and dreams about yourself sexually. It is clear that human beings are sexual from birth until death, that we are able to respond and enjoy sex throughout our lives. Your sexuality can give you pleasure and give your mate pleasure; it is a natural involuntary response to stimulation. The work of Masters and Johnson, the new information on the "G-spot" and female ejaculation, indicate that men and women are more alike sexually than has been previously thought. Both go through similar stages. In the excitement stage, the woman begins to lubricate and the man has an erection. Both of these are a result of increased blood supply. During the plateau phase, the tissues in the outer third of the vagina swell, the clitoris retracts and draws away from the vagina. For men, the testes increase in size and are pulled up.

During orgasm, women have a series of rhythmic contractions of their orgasmic platform—the outer third of the vagina and the tissues and muscles surrounding it. The number of the contractions, the interval between contractions, and the length of contractions produce the various intensities of orgasm. During orgasm the uterus also contracts. Men have similar contractions and also ejaculate sperm. Both men and women experience an increase in breathing rate, heart rate, and blood pressure. Ladas, Whipple, and Perry have found that women may release a fluid that is similar to male ejaculate, but, of course, without the sperm.

Both men and women have several types of orgasms. In women, orgasm can originate from the clitoris and involve the outer third of the vagina, or it can result from intercourse and involve the uterus. Orgasm may also entail vagina and clitoris together. You may have an orgasm in which the outer third of your vagina tightens and the inner portion of your vagina balloons as a result of the lifting up of the uterus inside the abdomen. Or you may feel as though your uterus is pushed down and the upper portion of the vagina is compressed. For men, an orgasm can be triggered by the penis or the prostate. The resolution stage follows orgasm, during which blood congestion and muscle tension disappear from the pelvic area and the organs return to their unstimulated state.

These stages remain the same from adolescence onward. As we age, there are differences in the timing of these sequences. For you males over fifty, the resolution phase may occur immediately after ejaculation, causing you to lose your erection and withdraw from the vagina. While it may take longer for you to become erect, there may be a much longer time between plateau and orgasm, which may have an advantage for your partner, as she enjoys several orgasms. And you, the woman over fifty, may find that it takes longer for your vagina to lubricate. After menopause, your vaginal walls will be thinner; use of a lubricating gel or (after seeing your physician) hormones can counteract this if it should be too annoying.

Many of you report that sex gets better and better as you get older. There seems to be a big jump in sexual abilities and reactions in women as they enter their thirties. As you age, you may become increasingly comfortable with your sexuality, and your body has been taught how to respond sexually. Additionally, women reach their sexual peak in their midthirties. As men age, they are more comfortable with their sensuality, and with their emotional feelings, which enhance sexuality; they are also able to maintain an erection without ejaculation for a longer period of time. In your forties, your female partner is comfortable with her own sexuality and well practiced in the art of climax. You are able to make love for a longer period. These factors enhance conditions for couple sexuality as you embark on a second honeymoon period in your relationship. Older couples, in their fifties, have reported that their sexual relationship is better than ever; they have more time, more freedom, and a greater appreciation of each other. So sex is something we can look forward to throughout our lives, and which, like fine wine, may indeed improve with age.

SEXUAL EXERCISES. The most important thing you can do

for yourself sexually is allowing and owning your sexuality. Next comes being aware of your sexual muscles. These muscles are widely appreciated in other cultures. There have been stories circulating for decades about women who could pick up objects from tabletops simply by manipulating their vaginal muscles. In the 1940s, Dr. Arnold Kegel rediscovered their importance for modern science. He was trying to find ways to help women who had difficulty containing their urine, without resorting to surgery. He taught them to strengthen their pubococcygeus, or PC, muscle and they reported back to him that their sex lives had improved dramatically. The PC muscle extends from your tailbone to your pubic bone, supporting your anus and internal organs, then runs around the rim of your vagina. It is the muscle that you use when you stop your flow of urine. It is the muscle that your dog uses to wag his tail.

The PC is one of several muscles which are active during coitus. The ischiocavernosus spreads out on either side of the clitoris or penis like an upside down V stretching down to end above the anus. It helps maintain the erection. The bulbocavernosus cuts off the flow of urine. It surrounds the opening of the vagina, diminishing its opening, and contributes to erection and ejaculation. Both of these muscles increase clitoral pressure with contraction. All of these muscles directly affect your orgasmic potential whether you are a man or a woman.

There are several different ways to exercise these muscles. Using a mirror, you should be able to see your perineum—the area between your vagina and anus, or testicles and anus—move when you suck in, as though you were stopping your urine, or push out, as though you were having a bowel movement. If you insert your finger into your vagina and contract this muscle, you should be able to feel it. Additionally, you can pull in or push out concentrating on the area around your urethra, your vagina, or your rectum. So there are two different motions for you to practice in three different areas. You can do most of the exercises outlined below anywhere, anytime, and no one will even know you are doing them. Try choosing something to remind you to contract your muscles, such as the telephone ringing, washing dishes, after urinating, or after intercourse.

FOR THE WOMAN

THE CONTRACTION. Contract and clench your muscles for the count of three, then release it for three and repeat for a repetition of ten. Increase the length of the contraction to ten seconds, then relax for ten seconds. You can begin with the front area, then concentrate on your vagina, and then on your rectum.

THE ELEVATOR. Use your PC muscle to suck in, imagining that your vagina is a building ten stories high. Bring the sucking sensation up slowly one floor at a time, then down slowly one floor at a time. You can do this with your anus, also.

THE WAVE. Contract your muscle starting from the front near the clitoris and focus on the muscle flaring out from the clitoris. Imagine trying to move your clitoris up. Clench the area between your vagina and clitoris. Then move the contraction between your legs to your anus. Try to clench all the muscles from your clitoris to your anus.

THE FLUTTER. Contract and then release your PC muscle rapidly, clenching for one second and then releasing for one second.

SUCKING. Imagine that your vagina is sucking in an object, and pull up in one smooth motion.

PUSHING. Bear down as though you are pushing something out of your vagina.

You may also insert objects into your vagina while you practice these exercises. Using an object will help your PC muscle increase in size and strength. The object can be a dildo, your finger, or any other suitably shaped object. You and your lover may also want to exercise together; you can try to suck your lover's penis deeper inside you and then push him out using your muscle. You may find that exercising your PC muscle is arousing. This is because after each contraction, blood rushes to the area and increases lubrication. You can use these feelings of stimulation to your advantage if you are trying to increase your sexual desire and responsiveness.

FOR THE MALE

Your PC muscle is in better shape than a woman's. Your penis is supported by this same muscle, and its strength determines your orgasmic capabilities, too. Some men have reported having multiple orgasms and also experiencing the sensation of orgasm without ejaculation following an exercise program for the PC muscle.

URINE STOPPING. Simply stopping and starting your urine exercises this muscle. Practice doing this until you can do it with precision.

PENIS TWITCHING. When your penis is erect, see if you can move it by twitching the muscles at its base. See, too, if you can twitch it when inside your mate.

MOVING THE TOWEL. Hang a light fabric, such as a handkerchief, over the shaft of your erect penis and twitch your penis, waving from side to side and then bobbing the fabric up and down. Now increase the weight of the fabric, using, say, a washcloth, a hand towel, and finally a bath towel.

DELAYING EJACULATION. You may have inadvertently conditioned yourself to climax rapidly. Perhaps when you masturbated you pushed yourself to orgasm as quickly as possible. Maybe your first sexual experiences were with prostitutes, who urged you to finish, or in conditions not conducive to leisurely sex. You may also hope that by prolonging your partner's foreplay, and minimizing your own, you will be able to last longer. The reverse is true. This is another case of getting more so that you can give more. You need to recondition yourself to delay your ejaculation by manipulation, then resting, then more manipulation. Have your lover arouse you by stroking your penis, then stop while you both rest. Then have her arouse you again and stop once more. You are learning to accept the feeling of extreme arousal. You learn that you do not have to climax but can lengthen that feeling of pleasure and passion before ejaculation.

You can also try the squeeze technique, which was perfected by Masters and Johnson. When your penis is erect, your lover locates the ridge of your penis and places her thumb on the part closest to your body. Her first and second fingers are on the other side of the ridge. Then she squeezes for three or four seconds with a lot of pressure. Your erection should subside somewhat. The two of you are inactive for half a minute before she starts manipulation again. Then she squeezes again when you feel the orgasmic urge. Repeat this several times—it will help you gain control over your orgasm as your partner learns to judge the various levels of your excitement.

The empathy you feel for your lover is one of the most powerful sexual tools you have. The pleasure you give her, the pleasure you see, feel, and hear your lover sharing is arousing. As you empathize with this pleasure, your own pleasure is enhanced, your sense of oneness and togetherness is strengthened. Feel her pleasure, involve yourself with her responses to you. As you concentrate on her, you will find that you're able to wait. Her ecstasy is the greatest inducement for delaying your orgasm; you are completely and totally interested in seeing your partner pleasured, fulfilled, and satiated. You think about her joy. Her joy is almost as important as your own, her contractions around your penis and the gush of warmth sings joy throughout your body.

Maintaining good PC muscle strength is something you can do throughout your life. It helps you to continue easy and enjoyable sexual contact and to maintain your orgasmic platform so that your body can give you the pleasure and satisfaction of orgasms.

THE G-SPOT. Many of you have reported an area inside your vagina that is particularly sensitive to touch. It is a spongelike material that surrounds the urethra. The G-spot is small, maybe the size of a dime, but swells when you are aroused. It evolved from the same tissue as the male prostate. If you lie on your stomach and your lover puts his fingers in your vagina palm down, you can feel the G-spot in between your pubic bone and cervix in the front wall of your vagina. If you lie on your back, it can be felt with his fingers palm up. You or your lover can place your palm on your abdomen above your pubic bone and press down to feel it. Some women report feeling as if they have to urinate when their G-spot is massaged.

When your G-spot is massaged, you may feel as if you are having vaginal orgasms, while massage of the clitoris creates the sensation of an orgasm originating in your vulva and the outer part of your vagina. It is possible, through intercourse, to massage both your clitoris and G-spot, which may give you the feeling of "coming" from your clitoris and vagina simultaneously. Some of you may ejaculate some fluid when you reach an orgasm, either a few drops or so much that you feel as if you urinated. You may feel your uterus contract during orgasm. There seems to be a range of experiences during orgasm. Some feel most of the intensity in the vulva, others inside the vagina, and still others feel a combination of the two. Some of you ejaculate fluid, and some of you have a special spot inside your vagina that is sensitive. All of these feelings are terrific. There is no particular way to come, no way that is better than another. Like the amount of love that you feel, the pleasure of one person's orgasm against another cannot be measured. You love as much as you can and you come with as great an intensity and as much power as you can.

IF YOU DON'T USE IT, YOU LOSE IT. It is clear that you will be able to enjoy sex into your eighties as long as you have an interested partner and have been having sex regularly. And here is one of the most important sexual findings, particularly for the long-term married couple. It is crucial for you both to continue to have sex regularly if you want to continue having it. A long period without sex, especially as you both age, may delay responses, as your organs and muscles need to be retrained to respond, to contract.

This was the problem that Olga and Oliver avoided. They were both in their early sixties when Olga had to have a hysterectomy. The operation was difficult for her and she had much anxiety about being able to function sexually again with her husband. Even though she had long since stopped menstruating, and she and Oliver had had three children, she felt she missed her uterus. She felt shy sexually with Oliver in spite of over forty years of being sexual with him—it was as though she were a different woman. Because of these feelings, she ignored his sexual overtures for several months. Oliver felt he was being considerate by not pressuring her for sex, feeling that she must still be sore. Oliver had read that it was important at his age to ejaculate regularly if he wished to continue being sexual. Although he felt like a teenager again, he had masturbated several times during the months when Olga seemed sexually disinterested. Finally, the two of them had a talk about their sexual relationship, and Olga expressed her sense of shyness and trepidation. They both reaffirmed that they were not ready to quit being sexual with each other.

That night, as Oliver and Olga prepared to make love, it was with a sense of embarking on a new adventure. Oliver's penis was certainly slower to erect than it had been when they were young lovers, and his erection did not become fully firm and hard until he entered Olga. She had some difficulty in responding. Olga had not masturbated since her operation and her muscles had become weak from lack of use. Together they recognized that she would need some more time to be orgasmic again. They had learned techniques for reuniting sexually after the birth of their children and used them. Soon Olga and Oliver were enjoying each other sexually again, demonstrating that they needed to maintain regular sexual expression. They agreed to remind each other to masturbate if one or the other should be "out of commission"' for some reason. They laughed that sex really was like riding a bicycle: you never forgot how, but if your legs didn't get any exercise, they might not have the strength to pedal you anywhere.

THE MORE YOU DO, THE MORE YOU CAN DO. Much of the new sexual information has strengthened this old truism. Although the head is the most important sexual organ, sexual activity is an athletic event. Just as a certain degree of physical fitness is necessary in order to be able to move with ease in the world around you, so a certain level of sexual fitness is necessary to enjoy sex. You can train for it, as you would for any other physical activity, and you can improve your performance. If you wish, you can devote yourself to the training so that you can perform at an Olympic level, in terms of both frequency and intensity of orgasm. Of course, many of you will not want to do this. You are not interested in training to run the 100 meters for the Olympics and you are not interested in training to be able to have multiple orgasms or have orgasms that last for many minutes. Many of you enjoy your orgasms just as they are, an intense pitch of rapture followed by release so that you feel as if you are totally filled or totally empty.

Each sexual contact prepares you for the next. Research has indicated that after ejaculation more testosterone is released in the male's body, preparing him for his next sexual contact. ingly, the amount of this male sex hormone is greater if he ulated with a partner than if he has ejaculated th masturbation. And for most of you, though there is a great feeling of relief from sexual tension the first time you have sex after a long period of abstention, the ease and power of orgasms increase with shorter time spans between sexual sessions. For both of you, the exercise of the sexual muscles happens each time you have an orgasm and strengthens the muscles of your orgasmic platform. So sex is like few other things in life. You can't wear it out. You can't do too much. It only gets better and easier with use. The more you do, the more you can do.

This was something Dawn learned. Dawn had always enjoyed sex. She enjoyed being held and caressed, cuddled. She loved the feeling of being rocked as Doug moved over her. Sex felt soothing and close. It truly seemed a way to show her love for Doug. She felt so powerful when she felt Doug's body tremble and contract, heard him moan when he came. Sometimes Doug would massage her clitoris to orgasm. She liked that, too, but that was not why she had sex. She had sex because of the intimacy involved. Because of the secret they seemed to share. She wished, though, that she could come with Doug inside her.

As Dawn grew older, she found her vagina becoming more sensitive. She loved feeling Doug move his penis in her, feeling him plunge in, hitting her back wall. She wished he could stay inside her always. She wished to have him in deeper and deeper, almost to the core of her. As she thought these thoughts, Dawn found herself imagining that she was sucking Doug deeper into her. She quivered as he withdrew his penis to the outside of her vagina and thrust herself to meet him, sucking Doug's penis with her vagina and trying to hold him fast in her core. She imagined milking him, trying to keep him filling her. Then she came, hot and fluid and full, feeling flutters and waves deep inside her. Dawn was thrilled with this new feeling that sex had brought her, she was glad that she had come through intercourse, so that for both of them it would have this added charge. She had climaxed through intercourse because she had moved in a different way. By contracting her muscles, and focusing on new sensations in her vagina, she had discovered a new part of herself, a new sexual skill . . . and delight.

Dawn found a book that detailed a series of exercises for her vaginal muscle. When she first read it, she was thrilled. It explained to her why she had had such a terrific response when she'd imagined sucking in Doug's penis. Without realizing it, she had been increasingly contracting her muscle, making it stronger and more powerful each time they made love, until it was so strong it contracted forcibly, giving her much pleasure. She decided to try the exercises and gave herself the training. One night she surprised herself and Doug by coming two times. It was as though she were at a peak of passion and could easily be sent over the edge again. Her muscles contracted vigorously against Doug's penis; they were so strong that he could feel her almost milking him and she was able to push him out of her vagina.

Dawn loved her new tricks and wondered how much more she could do. She and Doug found her G-spot and she realized that that was the area in her vagina that had always felt sensitive to Doug's penis. Even though she didn't know its name, her body seemed to have known about it all the time. Then she read that some women came many, many times, and some women even ejaculated. She wondered if she could push herself to do this, too. Maybe she could exercise more or get a biofeedback machine for her PC muscle. She certainly didn't want to miss out on anything. Then she stopped herself.

She enjoyed her orgasms just as they were. They were terrific! Sometimes it felt that if they were any more powerful, she would die from so much ecstasy. She loved her sexual relationship with Doug. It was more than she had imagined it could be ten years before when they were first married. And she had so much else to do in her life—her job, their children, her hobbies. This was enough. More exercise, more focus, would make sex feel like work. Her orgasms were powerful and fulfilling as they were. She realized she didn't have to try to do everything that had ever been done. Her sexual relationship with Doug and her sexual responses were not a contest. Sex was special to her because it was hers, something to look forward to. It was good enough. She did not want it to change.

Like Dawn, you can explore and challenge your sexuality. You can improve your performance. You can decide that you like it just the way it is. Your sexuality, your sensuality, is with you throughout your life. Appreciate your sensual self for what you are, for the glories in the world around you. Your pleasures are good enough in themselves. Enjoy the sensations you experience as you share your sensuality and sexuality with your mate. Feeling your feelings, and relishing them, empowers you. You feel strong and sure of yourself as a responding, sensitive person.

And for you, the long-term couple, the added part of your sexuality is the sharing of it with your lover. So that your lover's sensuality and sexuality are compounded with yours increasing the love and commitment which exist between you. Your pleasure bond grows as it is serviced by your sexual techniques and abilities.

3

DOING IT ALL TOGETHER

It had been one of those rare, perfect times. Charles and Carla spent the day alone together. A leisurely breakfast was followed by a long walk in a forest. They were dazzled by the whiteness of the birch trees. The sunlight turned green as it fell through the leaves. Charles cradled Carla on the mossy earth and they talked of feelings each had only guessed at in the other—fears finally spoken and accepted. At home they made love, fused into the same feeling and power. Moving together as one, they stared into each other's eyes, aware of the essence, of how exquisitely important they were to each other. They gave themselves slowly and totally. Their bodies were echoing and expressing their deep, loving feelings.

Carla was feeling terrific, energetic, on an emotional high. Charles had just finished running, was freshly showered, yet the dampness of his sweat still clung to him. How fabulous his buns looked under his towel, she thought. Suddenly she wanted him fiercely and grabbed him, pulling him into their bedroom. Charles had been feeling that a little quicky would be fun. Together they enjoyed their animal selves—using each other and being used for their mutual pleasure. The sex was hard and fast, the plunging and arching motions powerful and deep. Carla was sweating, clawing, pounding her body against his. Charles drove his penis deep inside her, grinding his pelvis against her, moving faster and faster. Later they lay back and laughed at the physical power and lust their joining had expressed.

Charles had had a terrible day. Work had not gone well, and he was anxious about a presentation he was giving the next day. He tossed and turned in bed, restless. He wished he could have sex to relax and finally fall asleep. Carla was lying next to him, engrossed in reading a novel, her lips pursed in concentration. By touching her thigh, he let her know he wanted to have sex. "How 'bout we mess around?" he said, the need and pleading in his voice. "Well, okay, but let's do it just for you," Carla answered. She put her novel down and let him have sex with her, giving him a loving gift. Charles felt released and relaxed after he'd had sex.

MAKING LOVE. As you can see, for Charles and Carla sex expressed different feelings. Sometimes it was the tender, exquisite love they felt for each other. Then, their joining reaffirmed their commitment to share their lives together; they felt the respect they had for the specialness in each other. They were truly making love at these times and using their bodies to communicate, to be close, to share the intensity of their caring and love for each other.

LUSTING. Sometimes their joining had the flavor of lust. It was as if they ceased being Carla and Charles, to be for that moment only man and woman. They relished the primal feelings surging through them, the force and energy sweeping over them so that they lost themselves, until they exploded into each other. They felt safe enough with each other to express themselves in this way. They knew each other's bodies, could provoke each other's passion and fully allow and appreciate the carnal aspects of each other. This was the "lusting" type of sex.

Their lusting took on a recreational aspect, for sometimes sex was just fun. The athletic nature of the physical act, the trying of different positions, foreplay, or games lent an aura of amusement. At these times it was neither the depth of the relationship nor the love and trust that was called upon. These were assumed. Instead it was their playfulness, their creativity, their adventurousness that were used to color their sexual interlude. They laughed, giggled, teased each other. They tried out new things, some they had only read about, and sometimes they resurrected previously tried acts for a second audition. They used their bodies and their sexuality for play.

HAVING SEX. There were times, too, when they merely "had sex." They were not making love, it had none of that intensity and sweetness; and they were not "lusting," it had none of that passion and demand for immediate powerful gratification. Rather, it was more like "getting off." The goal was orgasm, not expressing love or passion. Sometimes they would both have an orgasm, each bringing the other to climax. The joining then was product-oriented, the sex routine but pleasurable. Easy. Relaxing. Ordinary. It reaffirmed the elementary aspect of sex for them.

Sometimes, as in the example given, only one of them would be interested in coming. They had an understanding about how to solve the problem when only one of them wanted sex. If the disinterested partner was bone tired, or not feeling well, or needing space alone, then of course there would be no sex. But often, they discovered, one of them would want to be sexual and the other would be disinterested in climaxing but wanting to please the other. It seemed simple enough to do, and their experience together was so great they could easily satisfy each other. Sometimes, much to Carla's surprise, she would find herself becoming interested in her own orgasm after deciding to merely give Charles pleasure. Charles enjoyed giving Carla these "gifts," too, and would make love to her without being interested in coming himself. They chuckled that during the times when only one of them came, that partner had had sex. The gift-giving partner was making love, since the joining was an expression of deep loving feelings and the desire to please.

For Charles and Carla sex served many different purposes, had many different emotions. It was not always an expression of the loving feelings they felt toward each other. They were not always swept away by the passionate intensity of lust. Their sexual relationship did not always take on the routinization of a quick and easy coupling. Rather, it encompassed all these nuances of feeling, each type of sex reinforcing the pleasure bond and the sexual energy that flowed between them. They had accepted that the earth would not move every time they coupled, that sometimes there would be no orgasm, simply an exchange of closeness and love. However, they gloried in those times when the earth did move, when even the stars shook. They were comfortable and were able to admire each other's sexuality and yet not demand of it. How were they able to do this? They knew each other well sexually and were aware of their sexual styles. They had broken down the rules of sex and reexamined some of the "shouldn'ts" with which they had entered the relationship. And they nurtured their relationship, enhancing its strengths.

A friend of mine once commented, "A woman starts out making love and learns how to 'fuck,' while a man starts out 'fucking' and learns how to make love." There is a lot of wisdom in her comment. Some of you women may well have begun having sex for nonsexual reasons—because of the feelings you had for your lover, because of the exchange of closeness and affection that occurs during sex. With experience, you became more comfortable with the sexual process, more skillful, and your body learned how to respond. Then you began to feel the lusting feelings and used sex to satisfy your sexual itch. Some of you men may well have been with women for whom you felt little beyond the need to be sexually satiated. Later, as you became more comfortable with your loving feelings and your own emotions, you may have begun to use sex to express the tenderness and caring you felt for your partner.

As an adult couple you have the potential to experience all these feelings and to enjoy all the different types of sex with your partner. But perhaps there are blocks that impede you. Maybe you feel that sex must always feel like making love, or perhaps you are uncomfortable with your emotions, so sex is always "lusting" or recreational. Perhaps you believe that your sexual arousal and interest must be equal on every occasion. Your sexual relationship will reach its richest potential if it can encompass all three types of sex. This creates more variety, allows you both to express your love and passion (and to release sexual tension), and increases sexual frequency. Each expression strengthens the pleasure bond. Later we will look at how to break down the rules you may have about sex so that you feel free to make love, to lust, and to have sex. And you will learn how to ask for what you want sexually. But now, let's look at how the trust and passion between you have evolved so that you have a foundation for expressing your range of sexual feelings.

Couple Chemistry

Each of us seems to have built-in radar to help us find a sexual match. Plato believed that we used to be one four-armed, four-legged creature which the gods separated, leaving protrusions and notches. Each of us searches for the other part to complete our puzzle. Therapists are impressed with how often we discover someone to fit us perfectly. We unconsciously seem to "know" when we've met someone who will send all our chimes ringing or repeat a powerful pattern. When we meet that someone we are often astounded at how much alike, how complementary we are. This is no less true of our sexuality. You and your lover join your bodies to form a new entity and merge your sexuality to form a special couple sexuality.

Your merged sexuality is the basis of your pair bond. This unique part of couplehood is a combination of your physical bodies and your psychic sexuality. You fit well together—your bodies and your desires. You discover this when you meet.

YOUR MEETING. In your initial sexual meetings, you began to learn about each other's sexuality. Much of this took place without words, in a certain look or aura, a certain way you moved your body, a special kind of energy or quiet you projected. Without realizing it, you reminded each other of special people from the past, so that you felt comfortable, at home. You seemed to know things without words. You again experienced that feeling of ease and contentment. You learned about each other's sexuality in the silent communication that existed in each other's touch and the responses that touch created.

For most of you there was a period of intense sexuality in the beginning of your relationship. You may have spent days in bed, exploring each other, learning what most turned your lover on, discovering the unique erotic nature of your lover. You learned what your lover did that was most exciting to you. Perhaps you tried various positions and learned which were most pleasurable, the ones in which you seemed to fit together best. You began to develop a nonverbal vocabulary, a language of sex. Perhaps your lover would tap you lightly when he wanted you to be more gentle or to slow down. Then he would squeeze your arm hard when he wanted you to move faster or harder. Perhaps you could tell when your lover was close to coming because she raked her nails over your back or a slight moan escaped. Maybe you basked in the sweet scent of sex after your bodies were spent. The differences in your lover and the unique sexual self that your lover brings out in you are what make sex with each partner different. Making love with a new partner is almost like making love for the first time. Discovering new things about an old lover rekindles those feelings of excitement aroused by newness.

YOUR PHYSICAL CONNECTION. The two of you learned about the special ways your bodies molded together. Bodies and genital organs are different, they fit together differently. Each couple learns which positions feel best. Additionally, everyone has special places that are particularly sensitive. These physical attributes become part of couple sexuality. For example, perhaps your penis when it is erect lies flat on your stomach and your wife's most sensitive spot in her vagina is in the front wall. This would make face-to-face intercourse with you on top most satisfying to her. Perhaps your erection is more at an angle to your body, making a rear entry position most pleasurable for her. If this is also one of your favorite positions, then you fit together well. Perhaps you enjoy having your clitoris massaged during intercourse and are most aroused when you sit on top of your husband or when he massages your clitoris while entering you from behind. If your husband enjoys woman on top and rear entry positions, then you are sexual complements.

The angle of the man's erect penis, the most sensitive areas of the woman's body, and the size of the sexual organs and bodies are physical perimeters which you learned. Without realizing it you used this physical specialness to discover your most intensely pleasurable sex. By now you know whether your wife enjoys clitoral massage or pressure on her G-spot. You know if your husband gets more aroused by caressing you or by having you kiss his penis. You know if blowing in your lover's ear is a thrill or a distraction. You know if she groans with pleasure when you suck on her nipples. You know which positions send him into heightened ecstasy. Much of this is determined by what feels especially good to your unique body and becomes part of the foundation for your sexuality.

YOUR UNCONSCIOUS CONNECTION. As there are physical perimeters for your sexual relationship, so there are psychological ones. Each of you arrived on the doorstep of adulthood with a set of unconscious sexual symbols and images that were arousing to you. There are rhythms and gestures that excite and soothe you. There are sights, sounds, and smells that are invested with Eros. All these feelings and fantasies form a psychological portrait of your sexuality. You find the lover who partially fulfills these fantasies. Perhaps your husband likes large rounded backsides, and you have a large "tushie," making you forever a Venus for him. Perhaps your wife is turned on by large, callused hands like yours, which makes her especially aroused by your touch. Maybe she loves soft, open-mouthed kissing and so do you. All these images and preferred sexual activities are a combination of events from earliest childhood and previous sexual experiences which have become eroticized.

For Roy and Rena, the chemistry was there from the beginning when their attraction pulled them together. As they talked and shared their histories, they were amazed at how well they seemed to understand each other, how comfortable the communication was between them. When they made love, the sex flowed as easily as their shared secrets. Physically, their bodies fit well together. She loved his large size and felt comforted when his arms were around her. Roy enjoyed feeling powerful and protective, seeing her curled up beside him. Their sexual organs fit well together. His penis touched her most sensitive spot and her clitoris rubbed against his pubic area during face-to-face intercourse.

As their bodies molded in unison, so did their sexual souls. They remarked how perfect they were. Roy was only mildly interested in breasts, and Rena's did not seem particularly erogenous to her. But she became aroused when her abdomen and hips were caressed; her whole body tingled. And Roy adored the shape of her hips, cupping them in his hands as though to gather her all up. They both loved it when their bodies were fused together, joined closely and moving as one. They were so eager for intercourse that they hardly bothered with foreplay. They did not know why, perhaps it was the sense of a blurring of the boundaries of their bodies. Maybe it recalled how they were held tight and close as infants. But the way they moved together was like a song they were singing in perfect harmony. Roy's rhythm marched with Rena's preferred cadence—faster when she wanted, slower when she wanted to be teased, grinding into her when she wanted, and pushing in deep when she came. Joined as one and then separate again. She didn't know why she liked him deep inside her, but she did. He didn't know why he loved the feeling of being so closely united, but he did.

No lover can be the embodiment of all your symbols, but in a good sexual match the main thrust of unconscious sexuality is shared. And it is the presence of these elements that creates the chemistry between two people. You and your lover combine these unconscious sexual symbols, forming the richness and the connection of your lovemaking.

BUILDING THE PAIR BOND. As you both find sexual satisfaction together, your lovemaking is reinforced. You have invented a language of symbols and sounds, of smells and sights, which serves to enhance the pleasure you give each other, becoming even more erotic with each success. Sexual pleasure is a perfect reinforcement. The ecstasy that results from your lover's caresses, movements, or kisses imbues those actions with power to guarantee even more pleasure. When I was in graduate school I heard a story of a dedicated behavior-modification researcher who touched his wife's breast every time she had an orgasm. Soon, touching her breast made her increasingly aroused, so that after a number of years she learned to have an orgasm merely by his touch on her breast. I'm not suggesting that you use your marital bed as the setting for a psychological experiment! The point of the story is that gestures occurring at the same time as pleasure become endowed with a sexual power and symbolic meaning of their own. This is how your pleasure bond grows. A certain look in your husband's eyes may indicate to you his increasing arousal and the pleasure that will follow for you. The way your wife breathes and moans may let you know how close she is to orgasm and your final release. The nonverbal signals you send each other act like the baton in an orchestra, letting you know the rhythm and arousal flowing between you. These signals become especially potent for you. This is all so beyond your awareness that for a few moments you are one person feeling the same feelings, mentally and physically connected. You share a secret language of sex between you, and this is expressed by your sexual style.

Sexual Styles

The style you and your lover use was developed as a result of your unconscious connection and your physical pleasure. Probably each couple has evolved a sexual style as unique as fingerprints. Yet these can be categorized, although some may overlap. There are styles for initiating sex, styles for what the two of you do sexually, and styles for how much variety you have in your relationship. If you stop to think a minute, you'll recognize that you and your lover fit into one or more of these styles. And they are not cast in cement as the only way to approach sex; they have been developed between you both because they fit you.

INITIATION. Initiation styles can range from obvious requests to the most subtle games.

REQUESTING SEX. Beth and Barry always knew when one of them wanted sex. One of them would ask, "Do you want to make love tonight?" The other would answer, "Yes!" or, "Not tonight," or "Well, I don't know, convince me," or, "Okay, but just for you tonight." They felt secure when it was decided beforehand. Neither of them liked surprises, and for one of them to make a physical sexual overture to the other and be turned down would feel like rejection.

SEDUCTION. Kurt and Kay would never think of asking each other for sex. That took all the fun out of it. Besides, they each felt rejected if they were turned down following a direct request for sex. Asking felt crude to them. Instead they did a courtship dance, filled with subtle nuances of questions and answers. Perhaps Kurt would cook an especially delicious meal, or Kay would wear his favorite perfume. Sometimes they would tease each other or play fantasy games. Kurt would suddenly pretend he was a pirate about to kidnap her and carry her off into his captain's cabin. Kay would wear an especially sexy negligee. Each time the uncertainty of whether they were going to have sex made it more titillating. For them initiation became part of their foreplay.

FIGHTING. Dora and Dustin always seemed to fight before they made love. Sometimes these fights were play fights, in which they pretended to quarrel with each other. Sometimes they enjoyed wrestling on the floor. Dustin could feel Dora's breasts strain against his arm, and Dora could feel Dustin's penis bulging as he pressed against her back. The close body contact and straining against each other, feeling each other, were arousing.

THE MAIN EVENT. Each of you has also devised a different scenario governing what you do during your sexual contact to increase or guarantee pleasure.

THE FOREPLAY STYLE. Walt and Wanda loved to touch each other. They spent a lot of time kissing and then would slowly caress each other. They learned the art of sensual massage and spent time massaging each other with warm oil. Then Walt would concentrate on Wanda's breasts, rubbing and sucking on her nipples. She loved to stroke his penis, see it grow larger and larger under her hand. They spent a lot of time kissing each other's genitals. They would lie side by side, their heads between each other's legs. They loved the simultaneous lapping, sucking, and tongue tickling. Sometimes Wanda would climax while Walt was massaging her clitoris, then she would suck his penis until he came. Other times, they would arouse each other almost to the point of orgasm, then Walt would penetrate her and they would come. The focus on their sex was on the foreplay, it was their favorite part; but they often ended with their bodies joined in intercourse.

THE INTERCOURSE STYLE. Peter and Pam loved coitus. He could hardly wait to get inside her, and Pam wanted him to penetrate as soon as she was slightly wet. They kissed and caressed each other until they each felt the familiar sensations of arousal. Pam wanted to feel him enter her, and Peter loved being contained by her warmth. Once they were united, they would try different positions. Sometimes she was on top, or they were side by side, or her body would be at a forty-five-degree angle to his. Their bodies sang when they were moving together. It felt like dancing to them both. They used intercourse itself as their foreplay, and the orgasm would occur in one of their favorite positions.

THE TAKING-TURNS STYLE. Laura and Leon took turns sexually. One was the receiver and the other the giver. Laura yearned to lie quietly while Leon pleased her. He caressed her, stroked her, massaged her, kissed her until she climaxed under his touch or his mouth. Then it was his turn. He lay back on the bed while she worked over him. Often he climaxed while she was sucking his penis. Sometimes he would penetrate her and would come through intercourse. Sometimes he went first, and then they would focus on her pleasure. For them, taking turns was terrific; you were the sole focus of attention, you did not have to give to the other person while receiving. You could concentrate on your pleasure only, then turn your total attention on your lover.

VARIETY. The two styles below represent a continuum; each of you is at some point between these two extremes.

ALWAYS-DIFFERENT STYLE. Sylvia and Seth made love differently each time. They vowed not to have a routine and to use a different position for intercourse each time. Sometimes they would spend most of their time in foreplay, either massaging each other to orgasm or kissing each other. They enjoyed finding exotic places to make love and initiated each new piece of furniture in their house with sex. Each of them spent time figuring out new things to do and new ways to begin their sexual contact. They felt their sexual relationship was exciting because it was always different.

THE SAME ROUTINE. Nina and Noah loved their sexual style. They always made love in the same way. In the early part of their relationship they experimented with different things, and they discovered what was best for them. It felt so sure, so close and safe. It was like coming home to them. They expressed different feelings in the nuances of how they moved, and touched, and looked at each other. They did the same thing over and over, yet each time they made love it felt new. They were amazed that it never got boring.

AFTERGLOW. Just as each of you has developed styles for initiating and accomplishing your sexual episodes, you have also developed ways of sharing the afterglow. Perhaps you cuddle until you both fall asleep. Perhaps this is the time for your closest, most intimate talks. Maybe you softly caress each other. Maybe you rest awhile, then turn toward each other to make love yet again.

Together you have devised a sexual style that fits you as a couple. Yet you can add variety to your relationship by switching styles for a night. If you usually concentrate on foreplay, try the intercourse style. Perhaps you will discover new pleasures in moving together for a long period of time. Maybe you'd like to take turns, focusing all your attention on your lover. By trying another style, either in initiating or in what you do, you can add variety to your sexual relationship. Your sexual style can be used to make love, to lust, to have sex.

Now we will look at couple communication and how to feel free to use your sexual style to express a whole range of sexual feelings.

Couple Communication

Jill and Joshua found their sexual frequency dwindling. In the beginning of their relationship they were very much in love with each other, they only wanted to be together, sharing the world through each other's eyes. Three years later, they found their feelings had changed. They felt a new feeling of close companionship, of friendship, blossoming between them. But the intense feelings of infatuation had dissipated. Sometimes Jill still felt those old familiar butterflies in her stomach when Joshua leaned over to kiss her. When they made love, the sex was fantastic, always an expression of loving tenderness between them. But Jill didn't feel the same need to communicate her tender longings for fusion with Joshua through sex. Their lives felt so woven together.

The two of them had built a list of unspoken rules about sex that characterized their sexual meetings. They both had to want it, and they had to be making love, not simply expressing raw emotions of lust. As their lives got busier, and the initial period characterized by being in love waned, Joshua realized they were making love less. There were times when he wanted to have sex, times when he saw Jill slip on her stockings and imagined ravaging her on the newly made bed. Yet he feared acting on these impulses; Jill might be shocked, or furious with him. Perhaps it would tarnish the tender, making-love sex. Jill, meanwhile, was having similar fantasies. She sometimes wished Joshua would be swept away by blind passion and greedily take her. She sometimes wanted to give free rein to the more lusty side of herself but feared that Joshua might consider her unfeminine, unlike the delicate woman he'd married. They were both afraid to lose what they had, even though what they had did not service their relationship anymore. Their sexual relationship was at a crossroads.

The solution was apparent. They needed to communicate what they were wanting and break down their unwritten sexual rules. They each needed to take the risk—first by talking and then by trying new ways. Jill took the first step. Gently, and hesitantly, she described to Joshua her new set of feelings. It was hard for her, because she feared that he might feel criticized or he might view her as too interested in sex. But she figured she had only one life, and Joshua was her only sexual partner, and she did want to try it all. She wanted to be able to express these new feelings. She decided to make a move. She told him he had awakened new feelings in her, that he was teaching her how to respond more and more, and she sometimes felt like making love harder, more passionately. To her relief, Joshua was thrilled with the idea and said he'd been thinking the same thing. From then on, their sexual relationship began to express not only their loving feelings, but also the lust they felt toward each other. The frequency of their sexual contact dramatically increased.

You, too, may need to venture forth and take some risks in order to have a fuller sexual relationship. Are there things you long to try but are too timid to express? How do you know your partner is not sharing complementary wishes or fantasies? Certainly you may fear disapproval or rejection. Remind yourself of the old saying, "Nothing ventured, nothing gained." Making sexual changes is similar to making any change in your life; at some point you must simply put aside your anxiety and plunge in. And of course, after the first time it gets easier.

In your long lives together, your feelings for each other are going to change. Research indicates that the first period of a relationship is characterized by intense passion, feelings of being in love. These wane and are replaced by a loving companionship which grows deeper and stronger through the years. Since your feelings for each other are going to change, the feelings expressed by sex are going to change. If you accept this, and use talking together as a way to catch up and share the changes going on inside you, your sexual relationship wil continue to grow and express an increasingly wide range of feelings.

Yet many of you may have difficulty talking about sex. Perhaps you are terrified of revealing a part of yourself you have kept secret. First, you must decide you want to do it and believe that sharing your sexual feelings will improve your relationship. Examine your own attitudes about it; look at your own ambivalence. Then try to find out your partner's attitude toward the activity or feeling you are having. Sometimes ideas take a while to be considered. Give your partner some time—the length dependent on the attitude—and ask again. Try to find an easy way to say what you want. In the following chapter there are some games that may help. Eventually, though, you have to put it into words. If there is trust and respect between you, risking is easier. You may not always get what you want or ask for, but this does not make you or your partner a "bad person." By talking about your feelings and wishes and sharing vulnerabilities, you always grow closer. At first you may try something mainly to please your mate; later you may discover that you enjoy it for yourself. You may venture together into new territories, trying a new adventure you have heard or read about. Some of these things you will like, and some you will discard; some you will do only occasionally. Later on in this book there are suggestions on how to add new diversifications. As you broaden your sexual boundaries, you increase your sexual variety and your closeness.

There are several ways to help yourself, if asking for something feels uncomfortable to you. You already know how to allow and own your sexuality. You already know the hand gestures, which are excellent nonverbal ways to ask for what you want. But perhaps that hasn't worked and you need to put it into words. You have developed your own sexual language, and you and your spouse have a list of words you use when talking about your sexual organs or events. You are comfortable with these words. Here are some ways to ask for sex before, during, and after your sexual episode.

1. PRAISING. It is possible that you or your mate will find it very exciting to talk during sex. Some of you may find it erotic, others may find it only annoying or distracting. There are several ways to try out talking during sex. Praising is one way to start. Tell your lover how good it feels when you're touched and kissed in a particular way. You can give a running commentary, describing what's going on and how it feels, such as "I love it when you kiss me like that, soft and tender, your tongue tracing my breast and nipple. How I want to kiss you, too, touch your back and the cleft between your buttocks. . . . When you move inside me like that, teasing me, making me reach for you, I can hardly stand it. . . ."

Describing and praising can be as eloquent or as frank—even bordering on the vulgar—as you wish, as long as both of you find it exciting. Praising can help your partner to understand what you like sexually. This feedback stimulates excitement, as your lover feels gratified by your arousal. You may say, "It feels so good when you touch me like that," or, "Oh, is that terrific." Your partner will automatically do more of what you like.

2. ONE GOOD TURN DESERVES ANOTHER. This follows the maxim that states, "Do unto others what you *hope* they'll do unto you." You have something specific you'd like to do. Perhaps you really want your lover to perform oral-genital sex that night, yet you feel shy about asking directly for it. So you ask your lover, "Is there anything special you'd like tonight?" You are hoping, of course, that your lover will ask you the same question, so that you can then answer, "Yeah, I'd love it if you'd 'go down' on me." If your lover does not pick up on your clue, you can volunteer, with a statement such as "Well, I have something I'd love to do," or you can move on to number three.

3. "WHY DON'T WE . . . ?" This is a question that is really a suggestion. Your lover isn't put on the spot, but rather, you are buoyantly offering an idea that may be fun. Maybe you read about a new position in a book. "I was reading this book and the hero made love to the heroine swinging on a hammock. It really turned me on! Why don't we try it?" Perhaps you'd like to spend half an hour necking in the park or make love in front of the fire. Your lover may not think your suggestion is such a great idea, so don't feel hurt if it is greeted with less than overwhelming enthusiasm. If it's your idea, expect that you may need to take the lead. If you want to make love on a train, for example, and your lover agrees, arrange the time, buy the tickets, and so forth.

4. "I" MESSAGES. "I" messages are excellent ways to reinforce what your partner just did that was terrific or give her an idea of what else you would like. You can do this after you make love. Now some of you may feel that talking during the afterglow diminishes the peace and oneness. Others of you may feel that that is the time when you feel especially close and trusting. Your vulnerability is diminished and you are able to do your closest sharing. You know how you both feel about this. If offering even the mild-

est suggestion after sex would destroy the positive feelings between you, then pick another time. Maybe you'd have a few moments of quiet togetherness the next day or when you are out for dinner. Some of you may find that being in a car together makes talking about sex easier. Others may use a telephone conversation. If talking immediately after sex does not work for you, try another quiet, close time when vulnerability is reduced.

In an "I" message, you say what you like. You are expressing *your* opinion, you are not criticizing. For example, "I especially enjoy watching a woman slowly disrobe," or, "I love very soft touches on my clitoris, especially as I become extremely aroused." Note the difference between an "I" message and a "you" message: "You rubbed my clitoris too hard last night, and it turned me off. Please be more gentle next time!" This may only create feelings of inadequacy. You can combine "I" messages with "Why don't we . . . ?" or praising to become particularly effective.

"I really get excited when you move your hands on the shaft of my penis."

"I wish I could spend an entire evening making love to you. Why don't we get into bed at nine o'clock tomorrow and screw the night away!"

"Last night was terrific. I especially enjoyed the woman-on-top-of-man position. I like it when I do that one longer."

For some, these suggestions will work immediately. Others may need to repeat the request. Your lover might not feel like getting into bed at nine o'clock that night. It may take a while to percolate. Perhaps, in a month or two, your lover will have considered it and may feel more adventurous. There are some games in the next chapter that make asking for what you want easy and fun.

If there is some fantasy you are particularly desirous of trying, you may need to let your lover know. "This is really important for me. I want it for my Christmas present!" Your lover may not really be interested in your fantasy. Making love in a hammock, for example, may seem uncomfortable at best and make him seasick at worst. But if you announce that it is really important for you, then your lover can weigh your passion against her disinterest and make a decision. Certainly asking for what you want gives you the best chance of getting it. In addition, you are learning about each other and sharing your sexual selves. Being able to talk comfortably about sex is important in feeling free together sexually.

Feeling Free: Breaking Down the Rules of Sex

You have the potential to feel lust, to feel a deep closeness with your mate, and to want your sexual tension to be relieved. Allowing yourself to feel these feelings is the first step to expressing them. The suggestions in the previous chapter may help you to recognize your own feelings. Some of these are sensual, some more directly sexual. You also need to give yourself permission to act on these feelings with your mate. You must accept that it is okay to use sex to express a wide range of emotions. Then, without changing your sexual repertoire, you can add variety to it by changing the feelings you are expressing. Each of us comes into a relationship with a set of "rules" about sex. Some are not helpful to the sexual relationship or were helpful at one time and now need to be changed. Below are some of the rules you may have about sex that may be limiting your sexual relationship. You, too, may need to break down these rules in order for your relationship to be as full as possible.

OLD RULE #1: IT ALWAYS HAS TO BE MAKING LOVE.

IT DOESN'T ALWAYS HAVE TO BE MAKING LOVE. First and most important is that sex doesn't have to *be* anything. It doesn't have to be making love, it doesn't have to express unbridled passion, it doesn't have to lead to orgasm or even intercourse. You can decide to quit halfway and just enjoy the feelings of being aroused. You can go for a month without having sex and then spend four days in passionate ecstasy. You may have carried with you ideas about what making love means. What are these? Perhaps you feel you haven't really "done it" unless you've had intercourse. Maybe an orgasm, or simultaneous orgasms, proves to you you've "done it right." What are your ideas? How would it feel to try out a new definition of sex?

Maybe your sexual relationship would be more fulfilling, and would lead to greater closeness, if you'd loosen up these old ideas. You can use sex for whatever you two, together, decide. Sometimes it can be soothing, or passionate, or funny, or task-oriented (i.e., pushing for orgasm or for reproduction). You can change it whenever you both wish. Like Jill and Joshua, you may wish to make love and also have lusting sex. You may wish to gently stroke each other without the pressure of coming. You may decide, after starting to have sex, that neither one of you is as interested as you thought and quit. Whatever you want is fine. Your sexual relationship is for the two of you; you do not need to please anyone else. You certainly do not need to compete with some idea of what other people are doing. It can be whatever you want, as long as you both are happy with it.

OLD RULE #2: IT HAS TO BE MUTUAL OR MEANINGFUL.

IT DOESN'T HAVE TO BE MUTUAL OR MEANINGFUL. This "rule" may certainly have served you well in the beginning of the relationship, when sex represented a desire to communicate your love for each other through your bodies. However, it may be limiting you now. Both of you do not always need to be equally interested in having sex. One of you can be very eager and the other lukewarm. Both of you do not need to orgasm in order to make it a really good sexual contact. Sometimes giving the gift of pleasure to your partner may be enough; sometimes the sensual, sexual feelings feel good in and of themselves; and sometimes sex can mean simply having an orgasm and does not have to be a "meaningful" interaction between you both.

OLD RULE #3: IT HAS TO BE SPONTANEOUS.

IT DOESN'T HAVE TO BE SPONTANEOUS. You may sometimes need to schedule sex in advance, especially if your lives are particularly busy and you have found that sex is put on the back burner as you both rush around getting all your chores done. The first chapter discusses ways to schedule sex dates which may help the busy married couple.

OLD RULE #4: ALL MY WORK MUST BE DONE FIRST.

ALL YOUR WORK DOES NOT NEED TO BE DONE FIRST. Many of you may find that you have so incorporated the Puritan ethic that you are unable to make love until all your work is done or are only able to make love on weekends, which is a "play time" for you. You may find your mind is crowded with a list of things still left to do and that you are unable to get beyond those nagging voices to give yourself over to pleasure. This is a common problem, particularly in families in which both of you work outside the home. Then, each of you has your own list of uncompleted tasks, both at work and at home. You may feel guilty about not keeping the house as neat and clean as your parents told you to. You may need to persuade yourself that it really is all right to have fun before your work is done. Tell yourself that you deserve pleasure, that denying yourself sex will not get the work done, and that making love may give you a more optimistic, high-energy outlook.

Once you are convinced that you no longer need to subscribe to the Puritan ethic and that you can make love before all your chores are done, you must change your behavior and quiet any leftover nags to get up and work. Scheduling sex may be helpful here, as long as it doesn't become simply another task to perform. Perhaps you could spend some time really talking about the tasks or problems on your mind with your partner, which may lessen the pressure you feel about them. A long soak in the bathtub may ease the tensions away, or a massage could help put things in perspective. If this is really a problem for you, you may need to build in a transition between work and home, or between home and bed. You will need to find the transition that works for you. Possibilities include an exercise program; meditation; a sauna, whirlpool, or bath; a quiet, peaceful time alone; reading the paper; or having a drink.

OLD RULE #5: MY CHILDREN MUST BE ASLEEP.

YOUR CHILDREN CAN BE AWAKE. You can make love while your children are awake. Many of you may feel that you can only make love after your children are sound asleep, that they are not supposed to have any idea that you have sex. This will limit your relationship, especially as your children get older and stay up later than you do! Recognize the rules you have about sex because you are a parent. Do you feel compelled to make love with the lights out, careful not to make a sound? Do you completely forgo sex during the daytime? Do you also give up sex during vacations because you and your children are in the same tent or hotel room? What are the reasons for these rules? And how can you protect your privacy without endangering your sexual relationship? The two of you can go into your bedroom, closing and locking the door, and leave your children downstairs watching TV. There are suggestions in other places in the book on how to get around the booby traps of sex when you're a parent.

OLD RULE #6: I CAN'T HAVE SEX WHEN I'M MENSTRUATING.

YOU CAN HAVE SEX WHEN YOU'RE MENSTRUATING. Many of you may feel that it's wrong to have sex during menstruation. This is not a medical rule, but one of taste. It will not harm either the man or the woman to have sex during menses. Some women feel more interested in sex during menstruation, and there is some evidence that orgasm lessens cramping. So here, too, you can reexamine your attitudes about sex and decide if they need to be altered.

OLD RULE #7: I CAN HAVE SEX ONLY IN THE MISSIONARY POSITION.

YOU CAN TRY NEW THINGS SEXUALLY. All of you have taboos about what you feel comfortable doing sexually. Some of you feel more comfortable doing various things than others. Some of you may feel uncomfortable about oral sex, or anal sex, or about using vibrators or lotions. It is the philosophy of this book that anything the two of you, as mutually consenting adults in a long-term relationship, decide to try that does not cause bruises or welts, draw blood, or use bodily wastes as sexual objects is open for sexual exploration. You need to know what your rules about sexual variations are. Clearly, as long as you and your spouse have the same taboos there is no problem. But perhaps one of you would like to explore a new sexual horizon.

This was the situation for Thayer and Tina. Thayer had always wanted to try anal sex but was uncertain about Tina's reaction. He decided to ask her how she felt about it. Her mind seemed closed, she felt that it would be an invasion. Sometime later, Thayer brought up the subject again, asking her why she wasn't interested. She explained that she was afraid it might hurt, she was embarrassed about the idea of him feeling, or somehow seeing, her feces. She was afraid it would turn one of them off. They discussed the fact that there were many nerve endings in the anus, and that some people found it highly stimulating. Tina agreed to try. They decided to move very slowly, and Thayer reassured Tina that if she felt uncomfortable or embarrassed, they would stop.

That night, while Thayer was kissing her vulva, he gently massaged the outside of her anus with his finger, circling the tight opening. Tina was surprised at how good that felt. A few weeks later he slowly put his small finger in. His finger was lubricated and he knew to maintain an even pressure. Again Tina enjoyed it, realized how arousing the nerve endings in her anus were. Massaging and penetrating her anus with his fingers became part of their sexual play. Thayer was very careful not to touch her vagina with his fingers after they had touched her anus because he knew that that could cause a vaginal infection. Finally they decided they were ready for anal intercourse. Thayer had lubricated his penis with a gel and entered her slowly. At first it felt strange to her, somewhat confusing. Like vaginal intercourse, yet different. It also did not feel entirely comfortable. Thayer enjoyed the added tightness of her anal passage but found he also enjoyed the feeling of greater freedom and togetherness of vaginal intercourse. They decided they liked anal play, but that anal intercourse would be very rare for them. They had, however, added a whole new pleasure to their sexuality.

Like Thayer and Tina, you may enlarge your sexual horizons by reexamining your sexual boundaries. As you broaden your sexual boundaries, you increase your sexual variety and your closeness. In breaking down the rules of sex, you maintain a flexible attitude toward your sexuality; you are able to feel free to express many different feelings.

Relationship Strengths That Enhance Sexuality

Some of you will find that your sexual relationship marches alongside the rest of your relationship. When you are talking well, feeling close, sex is great. When you are preoccupied, or containing hidden angers, sex is mediocre or absent. Others will find that, regardless of the rest of the relationship, the sex is always good. It is there to help you get through the rough spots; when everything else seems distant between you, sex can serve to bring you close. The bond you had built when your relationship was good is expressed through sex and acts as a bridge until your relationship is again smooth. However it is for you, your relationship is the foundation of your sexual exchanges.

COMMUNICATION. Talking together is the most important activity you can do to enhance and maintain your sexual relationship. This cannot be emphasized enough. Good communication is essential to maintaining a relationship; conversely, lack of understanding and communication is one of the leading causes of divorce. In fact, recent research indicates that the only nonsexual predictor of a happy marriage is talking together. Communication is essential in maintaining closeness and understanding in all other aspects of your relationship, and it is essential in understanding each other sexually. Your sexual relationship is a microcosm of your relationship as a whole. If you cannot discuss your feelings about, say, your children, or a vacation, you'll have difficulty talking about your sexual feelings or asking for what you would like.

BEING SEPARATE PEOPLE. Seeing each other as separate people is crucial in a relationship. Yes, you are husband and wife to each other and your lives are interwoven, dependent on each other. You need each other to fulfill these complementary roles. But beyond that, you are friends, lovers, companions—separate people with separate lives, talents, and needs. You separate so that you can come together, sharing yourself, each caring about the other, respecting each other's differences. The trust you give allows you to be vulnerable with each other, thereby increasing closeness and trust. These foundations support your relationship and your sexual contacts.

Maneuvering between distance, intimacy, and fusion can be tricky. You can become distant and autonomous as you function in the outside world; intimate as you use each other for support, help, and sharing; and able to fuse during sexual contact. Fusion—forgetting yourself and becoming one with your lover—creates a powerful sexual contact. Neither of you is acting as a spectator, thinking about your performance or your lover's readiness, but you are so in tune, so close, you are like one person, satisfying yourself and your other at once. Yet for some of you this closeness feels scary. Perhaps you worry you will be swallowed up, that you, as a separate individual, will cease to be. Maybe you long for this fusion in all aspects of your life, long to cling to your lover; your lover may then feel suffocated and pull back. Perhaps you are already so fused that you cannot fuse further to effect a good sexual contact and so must create an artificial wall between you so that you defuse; then you can risk the closeness of sex and fusion.

You may be using distance and closeness to deal with fusion. Perhaps you pull away and withdraw after an intimate, close time together. Maybe you feel most excited when someone is angry at you or when you are angry. This may have an element of psychological sadism and masochism. You may need to hurt your lover's feelings in order to feel sexual and tender, or you may need to have your feelings hurt in order to feel accepted and vulnerable enough to allow the closeness of sexuality. If you are a couple who fights to kiss and make up, or a couple who creates a psychological or physical distance in order to have passion in your lives, you are, without realizing it, acting out your feelings about fusion, oneness, dominance and power, and psychological pain and vulnerability. Needless to say, these behaviors can harm your relationship. The power plays escalate, the pain intensifies, and the other aspects of your relationship may dwindle and erode. You may need some outside help so that you can become more comfortable with closeness and distance. You both need to be able to be close and intimate, and to be separate and autonomous to flower as individuals and as a couple.

SHOWING CONSIDERATION. Throughout the years, in a thousand little ways, you show each other consideration. Perhaps one of you brings the other coffee in bed in the morning, runs a hot bubble bath, buys a favorite dessert, or on the spur of the moment brings home flowers. Maybe it's a special smile, wink, or pat that stokes the fires of warmth and appreciation in the relationship. Affection can flow between you when you hold hands, kiss, sit close, smile into each other's eyes. All of these create an aura of closeness and physical comfort. It's icing on the cake if you also share hobbies—fishing, traveling, volleyball, going to the movies, walking in the park, raising tropical fish, anything that you both enjoy.

PUTTING YOURSELF ASIDE. Sometimes you put your own needs aside and focus all your attention on your partner's needs. Maybe she has had a recent death in her family, or he is concerned about aging and the effects on his health. There will be events in your lover's life that take precedence over your needs. At some point you will each need to focus your attention on your lover, generously and without resentment.

ACCEPTING THAT YOU WILL BOTH CHANGE. As you are able to accept each other's vulnerability and neediness, so you accept (and in fact glory in) your partner's changes. You did not marry a static person, one who would remain the same throughout life. Your ideas will change, your interests will change, your bodies will change. You will gray, wrinkle, get middle-age spread, get sad and angry, be sick. You will also grow in your profession, increase your competence, become more self-confident, feel joy, become thrilled, get wise. All of these are part of the human condition and all of these you can share with your mate. Doing so is a testament to your acceptance of each other's humanity, proof of your own maturity and self-acceptance. Your partner is not a Barbie or Ken doll forever fixed in plastic perfection, but a human being who grows, changes, and shares with you.

As you share the changes that occur throughout your lives, you share the changes of your sexuality. You share the increased passion, the various intensities of that lust, the communicative exploration. Your sexual style may alter through the years, you may try new things together as your taboos decrease. You feel the love and appreciation you exchange with your bodies. You feel free to do it all together, and together you trust and love and explore and enjoy.

4

WHOLESOME THRILLS: SEXUAL GAMES

Glen found himself fantasizing about new adventures and remembering past passions. His memory locked on and replayed a strip poker game back in junior high. What a thrill. With each hand the stakes became higher and higher, and you didn't know who would bare which new exciting part next. How thrilling, and what a torment—that glimpse of breast and thigh. His sexuality had been cloaked by a game. His heart had pounded with eagerness, his penis had throbbed with anticipation. Even losses were wins. He yearned to recapture that same feeling of unexpected sexual adventure, never knowing what was to be the next variation, in his marriage with Gloria. So he devised a game—request poker—combining the best of junior high strip poker with all the knowledge, education, and experience acquired through the affirmation of his adult sexuality.

Making the suggestion to Gloria was not difficult; she usually was willing to try sexual variations, and she loved playing cards, particularly if she won. The card game he imagined would be different: short card hands such as blackjack, poker, or gin, in which the victor would make a sexual request. Perhaps he would request the removal of clothes, kisses in specific places, or caresses. Glen was eager to try out his new ideas and, with a twinkle in his eye, approached Gloria.

They were beginning to undress for the night. It was early enough that they had time to spend together before exhaustion set in. Their children were sound asleep, they both appeared to have had an uneventful day. It seemed like a perfect night. Glen told Gloria about his new game idea and handed her a deck of cards. He wanted her to deal first.

Gloria agreed. "This is a crazy idea, but okay. Let's get this pillow out of the way," she said as they settled into sitting positions on the flowered bedspread. "How 'bout a hand of blackjack?"

"One hand or . . . ?"

"One hand," she said as she dealt the cards. "Oooh, you got the ace! Hit or stick?"

"Hit! . . . I'm good now," Glen said.

"I'm good, too."

"What'd ya get?"

"Twenty!" Gloria said excitedly. "I got a king, a three, and a seven."

"I've an eight, a five, and an ace . . . that's 14."

"Okay, I won. So I get to make the first request," said Gloria at her win, and she searched for an idea, giggling. "Let's see . . . I want you to take off all your clothes."

"All of them?" Glen said as they both laughed. "All at once?"

"All at once. Let's get down to the nitty gritty. . . . Well, on second thought, take off just your pants and your shirt."

"And leave me with my underwear."

"You can have your underwear and your socks on," said Gloria, laughing as Glen undressed, dropping his shirt and pants on the carpet beside the bed.

"I just took my clothes off. I was going to do it more seductively and slower. But you must be in a hurry tonight," said Glen, chuckling with anticipation. "Okay, my turn. . . . We'll play draw poker . . . five-card draw."

"How do ya play that again? I forget. Oh, I tell you how many cards I want?" she asked while he dealt.

"Yep . . . how many cards do you have?"

"I've got six," she said.

"I got six, too. Well, let's make it six-card draw."

"You say I'm in a hurry. Now you're so excited you can hardly count," Gloria teased. "I want two."

"Here's your two," Glen said as he passed them to her.

"I know I've got you beat," boasted Gloria. "And I almost wish we were playing for money."

"How do you know you have me beat?"

"I know I do. This is the best hand in a long while. I've got three fours and a pair of queens. What do you have?"

"I'm not going to tell you. . . . Well, I had two pair," he conceded.

"Okay, now I know what . . . how about if you kiss me; we'll keep you half-dressed."

"You're going to let me keep my underwear on, huh?" Glen said, pulling her toward him to kiss her. He started with gentle kisses on her eyes and finished with a long kiss, feeling her mouth with his tongue.

Beginning to warm from his kisses, Gloria said eagerly, "It's my turn to deal."

"I gotta get you out of your clothes."

"I know, but I'm on a winning streak."

"You're getting too cocky over there."

"No pun intended?"

"No pun intended," Glen said as they both laughed. "Now, let's get you out of those clothes and then see how cocky and boastful you'll be. You're looking pretty these days, though. . . ."

They continued to play. A few hands later, their feelings teased by the contrast of sexual activity broken by card playing, Glen lost another hand.

"I have a pair of jacks with ace high. Look, almost a royal straight. But let's pretend you won," Gloria suggested.

"How can we pretend I won?"

"Because we can. You said we can do anything we want."

"Well, then, I want the pleasure of taking your panties off."

"Okay," she said. "Too bad they're not edible."

"You gotta hold still now. Ease up."

"You want me to practice my pelvic tilts?"

"Later. . . . Hey! You're getting a gray pubic hair!"

"A gray hair," said Gloria, surprised. "No, that must just be a cat hair floating around."

"I don't think so. Your first gray pubic hair. That's neat. . . . Your deal."

Gloria suggested, "Let's play stud poker with the deuces wild."

"Okay."

"Oh, my God. Look at that . . . you've got three eights."

"I got more than that. You want to know what? I got four sixes. What did you have?"

"Nothing," said Gloria. "You won."

"Let's see . . . I want you to rub my back and shoulders. Caress them gently."

"Gently like this? Really gently, just with my fingertips?"

"Ahh, yes. That's nice. . . . It feels so good."

"Like little flower petals going up and down your back. You're sure it's not going to put you to sleep?"

"Oh, no. Quite the reverse. It's as if all my skin were alive," Glen said, his arousal evident.

"Where are the cards? Somehow we lost the cards. Oh, here they are," was Gloria's breathy response; her interest in the card game was diminishing.

"My deal, huh? Now I'm beginning to win," said Glen as he dealt a blackjack hand. "Okay, I won! I got twenty-one. I want you to come over here so I can kiss and caress your breasts."

While Glen was tugging on her nipple, Gloria said, "Is this as much fun as when you were in junior high, Glen?"

"Yes. It's a lot better than standing up and making love behind the schoolyard."

They continued to play, with Glen winning and undressing Gloria, then massaging her back. It was Gloria's deal and she decided to play blackjack. Glen won, getting five cards and twenty points.

"I want you to . . . let's see . . . kiss and caress my penis." Gloria moved her head to tongue the shaft of his penis and mouth the head. Their playfulness and teasing had increased their arousal, which was pushing them to climax. The card hands were becoming an increasingly annoying interruption as their lust and passion for each other climbed. Gloria won the next hand, remarking that she had felt badly for Glen when he was losing so often, but that now it seemed to balance out. She decided to stick with oral-genital contact, and Glen kissed and caressed her vulva and clitoris. By then, they'd forgotten about the cards, lost in a tangle of sheets and limbs. Gloria wanted only for him to be inside her, and Glen wanted to feel them move their bodies together. Later they decided that request poker would remain part of their sexual repertoire. It was definitely more fun than Monopoly or video games.

You, too, can play request poker. The rules are easy—card hands interspersed with sexual requests. The victor of the card hand wins the right to make the sexual request. The equipment is inexpensive—simply a deck of cards, your two bodies, and imagination. The game is as individual as the couple. You may use it as you both wish. It can be used as foreplay, as Glen and Gloria used it. Perhaps another couple could use it as the entrée to their sexual act—one requesting oral sex to orgasm, the other a specific intercourse position. Request poker can also be used to play out a fantasy, such as one partner watching the other masturbate, or for telling a sexual story.

The beauty of the game is that it is a doorway into sexual wants. Since it is easy to ask for something when you've just won that right, shyness decreases. At last you can ask your lover to kiss your toes or try putting a finger in your anus. It can make asking for what you want sexually lighthearted and fun. What you request is what you feel would be exciting at that time, giving your partner new clues regarding which acts are most exciting for you.

Sexual fantasies and longed-for acts vary over the decades. For some of you, the shyness, inexperience, and naiveté of your youth have evolved into a mature acceptance and eagerness to try new things. Your sexuality and confidence have grown. Acts that once felt new and adventurous are now old hat, part of your sexual repertoire. Oral-genital contact, once a new way of being close and a novel sexual thrill, may now be part of your usual foreplay. You may desire to explore new arenas of sexuality with your loved and trusted partner but still be slightly timid about letting your lover know your new ideas. Request poker helps resolve this shyness.

Since request poker is a game that is tailor-made by you and for you, it is as individual and unique as each couple. But there are also some universal elements that make it so much fun—like surprise. You never know what your partner is going to request next. Will your lover want you to do something? Or will you be the receiver, savoring attention in some unpredictable way? Your lover may come up with a brand-new idea, or perhaps you will request the realization of a fantasy. The element of surprise is a terrific antidote for a relationship in which sex has become bogged down by routine. Even if you perform your usual sexual routine, the interspersing of the card hands and the winning automatically lend a hint of the unknown, of flirting with sexual danger and excitement. It makes it seem new again. This dash of unpredictability recaptures the feeling of innovation and adventure—much like a trip to a new place, though a lot cheaper.

The card playing lends an element of play, and your adrenaline increases with suspense about winning. This is in itself sexually arousing. Play evokes teasing, and the teasing and surprise recharge your sexual interplay. Request poker is ideal for those of you who like to win but can subordinate your lust to win at cards to your sexual lust for each other. Trust is also a crucial factor. New sexual ideas should be encouraged; but as with all sexual activity, an idea that stimulates only disgust in your partner needs to be exchanged for one that will enhance closeness and passion. Request poker is a safe way for you to explore new variations with your mate.

You can use this as a springboard for all sorts of ideas you generate as a couple. Perhaps you hate cards and would rather play spin the bottle or post office. Maybe video games—or, perhaps, Scrabble word points, Uno hands, or pin the tail on the donkey—could be interspersed with sexual activities. Any relatively short game or contest that you enjoy doing or remember being fun when you were a child can be adapted. The game and the activity are dictated by the fabric of your relationship, how you feel, and what the two of you as a couple enjoy doing. It is designed by you and for you—a new game for the two of you to invent together.

LOVE NOTES. Love notes, love letters, cards—how you loved to get them in your youth, in the first flush of flirting and love. Back in those days you might have penned a long letter describing your feelings for your beloved, praising your mate and letting your partner know how much you adored and appreciated your new relationship. You wrote of the thrill of his kisses; the press of her body against yours. The churning and blossoming of feelings were more powerful than you had even imagined but seemed as inevitable and powerful as the tides of the sea and the glow of the moon.

Twenty years later those feelings are often deeper still and an integral part of your lives. You show your feelings in perhaps a thousand little considerations. You may say daily, "I love you," you may bring him coffee in bed, tell her how beautiful she looks as she hurries off to work. Yet the scope, depth, passion, and comfort of the love you feel is assumed instead of described. How much more impressive and important is a love letter after two or three decades of love. It is an obvious expression of passion, yet is often forgotten as the years go by.

Write down your feelings and present your lover with a love letter. Perhaps you will feel awkward about it at first, as if you're suddenly pretending to be a schoolgirl or young lad in the first throes of infatuation. But as you write, you will find the appropriate words so that you express the mature, wise love tempered by experience and time. You need not be eloquent, only sincere. You may mention something you appreciate and admire about your lover or some nice consideration that was performed. It need not be long, a simple "I love you, darling" may be enough. You could mail it, perhaps trying to change your handwriting so it's not obviously from you. You could tuck it into a pocket, briefcase, lunch, socks, purse. A loving surprise.

Valentine's Day, birthdays, and anniversaries are perfect times for this; they remind you to communicate your feelings, nudge you to express appreciation and love. When you first fell in love, every day was Valentine's Day; your lover was constantly in your thoughts, and you let each other know of this psychic attachment and intensity. An unexpected love letter is a way to recapture this feeling. A love letter may be even more valuable coming as a surprise, out of sync with expected dates or yearly routines. Maybe it's inspired just because it's raining and that reminds you of the night you got drenched together and wandered around laughing because for once there was not a taxi in sight. Or perhaps you and your lover had made love particularly passionately the night before or tried something new, or your lover was especially helpful with a business problem.

Some of you may feel you'll never be able to find the correct words to express your emotions; you're afraid you'll sound maudlin and childishly mushy, and you'd like to hire a Cyrano de Bergerac to eloquently voice your love. The card industry has recognized this need and provides you with many choices to express your feeling in words and pictures. A romantic card or flower, like a love letter, says, "Hey, I love you!" with a big red bow around it.

The card shop has an array of cards, from the romantic, to the suggestive, to the vulgar, and your mate might get a kick out of a surprise card sent to him. Perhaps you'd like to write a little note telling him he cooked a great meal the night before, wish her luck on a speech she's giving. Your mate may get a kick out of opening an envelope at work to find a three-foot card screaming, "Fuck me! Fuck me!" in vibrant colors. Love letters, cards—romantic or suggestive—notes, flowers, even the first green buds of spring or Indian corn are all special ways of letting your lover know how much you care and appreciate your relationship. You are courting your lover all over again, rekindling the spirit of romance. This reminds both of you of the sexual magnetism, lust, and love that flows between you, thereby enhancing it.

EROTIC MONEY. Erotic money is a written sexual request—i.e., for one-half hour of necking in the backseat of the car, for a bed picnic, for oral-genital contact, and so on—which you give to your partner. Some examples of erotic money are made up for you in Appendix B (page 245). Erotic money can be used in many different ways. You can tie the bills together with a ribbon and give them to your mate as a present for her to hand back to you when the mood hits her. You may wish to tuck them away in a drawer to hand to your mate at an opportune moment. Weaving them around a quiet dinner at home for two, you may farm the kids out to a friend's house for the night and start with one-half hour of necking, move through a sensual meal of your favorite foods, and then deal the erotic money as you wish. You can put them all in a hat and draw them out one at a time, following the directions on each of them. An open-ended sexual game, erotic money can be used as you wish to add variety to your sexual relationship.

THE SEXUAL BET. This is a quick and simple game. You may set up a teasing challenge about whether it is going to rain on the day you plan a picnic, or if the dinner guests are going to arrive on time. Almost anything is open to a bet. The sexual bet simply makes a sexual activity the prize. For example, you may bet a kiss if the movie you wish to see is not sold out. A dinner on the town, paid for by the loser, may be bet if your favorite candidate wins an election. You may bet intercourse on demand if an investment pays off or if your team wins the Super Bowl. The sexual bet benefits the entire relationship and adds a little sexual spice. It is also a great way to show acceptance and to joke about differences of opinion. Some things are not worth arguing about (such as who's going to win the election, or making predictions about a certain stock); here, a bet ends the argument, and with a sexual bet, everyone wins.

Teasing Games

"WILL YOU OR WON'T YOU." You played this game all the time when you were a virgin, before you had decided to commit yourself to a new sexual relationship. You wanted to be sexual but hadn't yet consummated. You both were going two steps forward and then one step back, resting, heightening the passion between you. You were never sure when or if you would complete the sex act. Just so much "yes" to keep the passion going, with a dash of "no" to slow down the pace. This lack of certainty, this ebb and flow of sexual excitement, supplied some of the intensity in the early part of your relationship. The challenge and the chase were exciting.

Obviously, maintaining a question of "will you or won't you" in a long-term permanent marriage can be difficult. You both must know that you will and that the initiation of sex will be easy rather than a contest each time. Still, there are ways to increase the seductiveness and the teasing aspects of initiation of sex without becoming a "cock tease" or undermining the trust between you.

When Tina wanted to make love with Tom, she would put curlers in her hair and goop on her face. She was a virgin when they married—at least technically. They had done everything imaginable except have intercourse. Tom had been aroused by her withholding—almost, but not quite, giving herself totally to him. He loved the act of conquering her over and over again, never knowing when she would allow him to have her. After they were married she maintained the pretense of being conquered. She would wear her shabbiest bathrobe, make herself look an absolute mess, and then go about her business, ignoring Tom. This show of disinterest aroused Tom and he could then "reconquer" her. Moving closer to her, he would rub her shoulders and cup her breasts, seducing her and reaffirming his attractiveness and sexual power.

How can you and your lover heighten the seductiveness in the initiation of sex? How can you tease your lover as part of the seduction and walk that line between a teasing "maybe" and a rejecting "no"? The game must be suited to the particular couple. You know what will entice or turn off your mate. Your lover's reactions through the years have taught you. Does your lover enjoy the thrill of the chase, or does he interpret the first "maybe" as a "no," needing more feedback that you are turned on? The interplay must be between "seduce me" and "check and see if I'm interested," not between "I don't want you tonight" and "well, I will if you insist."

You may want to use dress as part of the seduction, as Tina did. She dressed sloppily, but you may want to dress sexily and then pretend that sex is the last thing on your mind. A romantic dinner—table all set with candles and flowers, children off for the night—may be followed by a pretense of business at the dishwasher. You may start kissing hungrily and then remember you forgot to take the clothes out of the washer. Alternate suggestive statements or movements with everyday ones, so that your partner isn't sure exactly what is on your mind. You have to feel your way about what is successful here. Too much withdrawal and your partner will believe you really aren't interested in sex that night and give up.

"I WANT YOU, BUT WE CAN'T MAKE LOVE HERE!" You can also tease your partner by showing sexual interest in a location that makes sexual relations impossible. Lydia was terrific at this. She and Len got on an elevator, and to her delight it was empty. She tickled his earlobe, ran her finger down his neck and shoulders. The elevator stopped, the doors opened, but no one got on. She then moved her hand to his penis, stroking it through the fabric of his pants. "What are you doing to me?" Len pretended to complain. Again the elevator stopped and a woman carrying laundry got on. Lydia backed up to him, pressing against him, pushing her buttocks against his crotch, all the time acting as if she were merely trying to give the woman lots of room. By the time Lydia and Len got to their floor, they were so excited and giggling that they could hardly unbolt the locks to open the door to their apartment.

There are scores of inappropriate or impossible places, some made famous by literature and the movies. The eating scenes in the movie *Tom Jones* show the erotic use of food. Restaurant scenes—such as in *Flashdance*—show how petting can be carried on under a table. The program notes or a coat at a concert may make excellent cover for caressing. A workplace can be a location for an interlude of sexual stimulation prior to lunch, a visit home, or a stop at a hotel for an afternoon matinee. "Will you or won't you" and "I want you, but we can't make love here!" are ways to sexually tease and heighten sexual eagerness.

"I'M NOT GOING TO LET YOU COME." Wendy and Will were feeling bogged down by their sexual relationship. It was too routine and had become unexciting. If only they could recapture the curiosity and hunger that they'd had for each other before they had ever made love, if only they could regain the passion and intensity they'd had when they had first started making love. Maybe they should start all over again, they thought, and pretend they were a new couple. Together they devised a plan, a lengthy teasing game to which they both agreed, hoping it would increase their lust. For the first week, they were only allowed to "neck" and touch each other through their clothes. Wendy had forgotten how terrific simple kissing could be, and they both polished up old skills, softly kissing each other, exploring lips and mouth with their tongues. They rediscovered the neck and ears as erogenous zones, touching, pressing, kissing, and sucking. Wendy got a "hickey" for the first time in twenty years.

During the second week they were allowed naked body touching and kissing, although they had agreed that genitalia were still off limits. Stroking, massaging, and kissing made each of them aware of their lover's body parts (and their own) in new ways. Wendy discovered the sensitivity of the backs of her knees. Will had never been aware of how arousing it could be to have the inside of his arms gently stroked till his flesh responded with goose bumps. Their thirst for each other was increasing; they were eager to move on to the next step. Each of them felt frustrated and found that they thought about making love with each other constantly. The third week could not come soon enough. Finally they joined with the passion and lust that they'd had in the initial consummation of their relationship, plus the depth that years of knowledge had brought.

They certainly did not want to let this impatience and passion diminish, so they figured out some ways to continue to tease. Will had a great idea. He could sense when Wendy was most desirous of him during intercourse. Her motions would be faster. Will withdrew his penis to the lips of her vagina, forcing her to beg with her body to have more of him inside her. Wendy would arch her back, trying to suck him in with her vaginal muscles. Will plunged deep inside her for several strokes, giving her what she wanted, and then again withdrew. Deep thrusts were followed by slower, shallower ones. Her increasing ardor and his teasing her by giving her what she wanted and then withdrawing made her passion explosive and her orgasms powerful.

They had carried the game of teasing into the motions of intercourse—Wendy became increasingly eager to come, and Will's withholding enhanced the need for more. Will later read of a similar technique used as a sales approach. You offer the buyer an object, and just when he's really interested you withdraw it, implying that you don't really want to sell it to him. This convinces the buyer that he must have it, and the sale is made.

Wendy responded fully to Will's new techniques, impressed that they had reached a new stage sexually. She wanted to reciprocate with a game of her own that would encapsulate their three weeks of sexual foreplay into a shorter span. She began by kissing and touching Will's clothed body. Slowly she undressed him and caressed the perimeter of his body. She touched, massaged, and tongued his feet, hands, arms, and legs. She moved slowly into ever smaller circles, as if his penis were the center of a target, a target that must not be touched—it was the only area of his body that was not pinched, rubbed, licked, and caressed. Will's hunger to have his penis touched was all the greater. The attention to all other parts of his body had increased his focus on his penis. Finally Wendy turned her attention to Will's penis, stroking, kissing, and sucking. Will reached the point of orgasm; Wendy stopped, rested, and then resumed slowly. Again he was brought to the peak of climax and left hanging. Finally, the tension and arousal burst forth in a powerful, lengthy orgasm.

Wendy's and Will's discoveries can be used by you, too. You, too, may "go back" and start all over, rediscovering erotic sensations and refocusing attention on nongenital parts of the body. Decide how much time you wish to spend. Wendy and Will decided on a week for each stage, but you may wish to spend a few days at each stage. You also need to decide on the nature of each stage. Wendy and Will had three: necking, touching and caressing without clothes, and finally sexual union. If you wish, you could add clothed petting and genital touching (but not to orgasm).

Then, set aside a time to be with each other that is quiet and unlikely to be interrupted.

You can also use the technique of movement withdrawal, either during intercourse or as a foreplay to heighten hunger. You can tease your wife by the varied depth and rhythm of your motions during intercourse. Pull out your penis so that only the head is in her vagina. Then thrust in deeply for several counts. When you sense that she is most eager for you, withdraw again, making her ache for you. You can tease your husband the same way. You can use caresses or oral-genital contact, stopping when he is most excited. You can move your body so that he can't be deep inside you when he really wants to be. As your lover approaches climax, use those motions that are most exciting, at last giving what your lover wants most. There seems to be a natural rebelliousness in many of us, and the "I'm not going to let you come" game is met with a defiance to come more, bigger, and better than ever. The game sets up a challenge and your lover becomes determined, eager, and insistent on proving you wrong, guaranteeing orgasm.

In and of themselves these games add play, laughter, and joking. They reveal new parts of yourself to your lover and increase the psychic closeness and understanding, strengthening and augmenting the sexual bond. They will help you discover new varieties of activity. And lastly, they are fun.

BAUBLES AND GADGETS—XXX-RATED TOYS

Marcia had learned to masturbate with a vibrator as a teenager. Her parents had a "Swedish massager," which they'd used for back rubs. Marcia wanted to reduce the size of her thighs by massaging them with the machine—much like those electronic spot reducers she had seen advertised. As she was rubbing the tops of her thighs she noticed the titillating feelings the vibrations were sending to her clitoris. Placing her hand and the massager over her clitoris, she masturbated to orgasm. She was surprised at the powerful feeling it gave her; she felt breathless and excited. Needless to say, she quickly forgot about using the massager to reduce her thighs! She had discovered something much more fun she could do with it.

After she married Mark she stopped using the vibrator. It somehow seemed wrong to masturbate when she had a partner—she felt her partner should be enough for her. And she feared Mark would interpret a suggestion that they use a machine as a criticism of his lovemaking. Their sexual relationship was good. Mark always satisfied her, though she was not able to come during intercourse. He would touch her or kiss her clitoris until she came, and then he would come during intercourse. She knew that many women—perhaps most—did not reach climax during intercourse and argued with herself that she was fortunate that Mark was such a considerate lover and also fortunate that she was orgasmic. Yet she longed to be able to come with him inside her, to be able to share that moment of ecstasy simultaneously.

She expressed her longing to Mark and was surprised when he suggested they use a vibrator. He, too, confessed that he would love to feel her come while he was inside her. They decided to try to learn this new ability together. They bought a vibrator and started discovering its possibilities. Mark watched her masturbate; he then used it on her to orgasm. They were becoming comfortable with the vibrator as a new sexual tool before trying to alter their sexual pattern. Then, one night, Mark aroused her as usual but stopped short of orgasm. Feeling very excited, Marcia sat on top of him, his penis inside her and the vibrating head on her clitoris. After a few tries, she was able to come this way. That was a terrific night for both of them! Marcia loved the feeling of coming with him deep inside her and Mark could feel her vagina contract and gush with fluid. They experimented with several other positions in which they were able to use the vibrator during intercourse. When Mark entered her from the rear while they were both lying on their sides, she was able to place the vibrator so it stimulated her clitoris and Mark could feel the vibrations in his penis. Another position in which Mark lay on his side and Marcia lay on her back with her legs over his hips also worked.

After Marcia was able to come using the vibrator they began to rely on it less and less. Sometimes they would remove it just before Marcia was ready to orgasm, and her excitement was so great that she came without it. Then she began to love the feeling of his body pressed close to hers. With more practice, they learned to come during intercourse without using the vibrator at all.

Marcia and Mark had used a vibrator to enhance their sexual relationship. She had used the vibrator to teach her a new way to be orgasmic. You, too, may wish to experiment with the new sexual equipment available. But you may have some feelings that impede acting on your curiosity. Perhaps, like Marcia, you feel your lover and his body should be enough for you. Look at a sexual aid as a way for both of you to add variety to your sexual relationship or to solve a problem you are having. In any case, it is a tool that can add to your fun. You may also fear that you will become dependent on a vibrator—addicted to it, and will need it in order to orgasm. If you're already orgasmic without it, that clearly won't happen, but you will have discovered another way to climax. If you are not orgasmic, vibrators are helpful in teaching you how to be. Then you can learn ways to use the vibrator in your lovemaking and maybe eventually you'll be orgasmic without any aids.

Many people are tossing aside their inhibitions about lotions or sexual gadgets as increasing numbers are using them in sexual relationships—91 percent of women, according to one recent poll. Maybe you have traditionally used a lubricating jell. Maybe you have used a vibrator to increase orgasmic potential. In fact, many women first became orgasmic through the use of a vibrator or reached orgasm during intercourse with the help of one. Some of you may use gadgets to delay ejaculation or maintain an erection. Some gadgets make the sexual foreplay unusual or more fun. In addition, there is a new sort of sexual aid which exercises the PC muscle, increasing vaginal sensitivity and orgasmic potential. Many of you are becoming familiar and comfortable using gadgets to discover different means of becoming satisfied sexually and new ways of playing sexually.

Perhaps you are torn between an increasingly confusing array of sexual paraphernalia. "Everything that is good can be made even better," imply the creators of sexual equipment. You can adorn your penis, tighten your vagina, entice like Aphrodite with your aroma, shake and vibrate to the softest quiver or the deepest thrust. Some sexual gadgets feel exciting in their very novelty, or forbidden, or sleazy. Some are cloaked under the guise of science or health. In the porno shop, their are displays of equipment, some intriguing, some comical-looking. Supermarket magazines show photographs of a woman massaging her face with a phallic-shaped massager. With the invention of the small battery, many ancient sexual toys have become vibrators. All these consumer goods—

some in use for centuries and some the result of modern technology—are available for your sexual experimentation, excitement, and knowledge.

You can buy sexual paraphernalia from several different sources. The most available source is the porno bookstore, which often carries vibrators, lotions, and artificial vaginas in addition to its customary pornographic pictures and prose. There are also sexual boutiques which are designed to appeal to women and couples. In a boutique, there is none of the ambiance of "sleaze" often found in a porno bookstore. Rather, they are similar to any other chic retail establishment. They are well lit, colorful, and display merchandise in attractive ways. They do not carry hard-core pornographic visual materials, but more erotic, artistic sexual pictures. Some are committed to feminism and see sexuality as part of a total philosophy of freedom for women. Sexual boutiques also carry a wide variety of equipment, lotions, and jells. Lingerie is also featured, some sensual and some the nippleless, crotchless variety. Items appealing to the humorous side of sex also abound—there are lollipops shaped like penises or breasts and ice cube trays that form your ice cubes into naked women or penises. There are joke books, cartoons, and wall plaques. Sexual boutiques are like any other boutique, which helps you feel comfortable enough to walk in and browse.

Or you may prefer the privacy of mail-order catalogues. Xandria Collection, P.O. Box 31039, San Francisco, CA 94131, has a tasteful, informative catalogue of toys, lotions, underwear, and books for $3. Eve's Garden, 119 West 57th Street, Suite 1406, New York, NY 10019, also does a mail-order business. Uniquity, 215 4th Street, P.O. Box 6, Galt, CA 95632, sells sexual aids and materials for psychology, education, and recreation. All catalogues assure you that your purchases come in a plain brown wrapper so that not even the postman knows what you've ordered.

And last, the lotions and gadget market has invaded the Tupperware party! There are several companies that market their products much like Tupperware through home parties. Here you can invite your friends, play games with sexy overtones, look over the merchandise, and buy what you want. Ninety percent of the partygoers are married women trying out new toys with their husbands. Sensation Parties, Inc.; Just for Play, Ltd.; UnderCoverWear; and Nice and Naughty, Inc.; are all companies that sponsor sex toy parties. Look in the Yellow Pages under "Home Demonstrations" or "Home Parties" to find out what companies sponsor sex toy parties in your area.

Most of the lotions and gadgets are obvious in their purpose or come with instructions. You need to add your common sense when you use this equipment. Do not use a vibrator if you have any unexplained calf pain. Make sure all the parts that go inside you are clean by washing them first. Use a lubricating jell on plastic items if they don't slide easily. Don't use electric appliances near water. Don't put anything inside you that you won't be able to pull out—you wouldn't want your lovemaking session to end in the emergency room of the hospital to have an object retrieved from your anus. Never put anything in the vagina that has been in the anus without washing it first. This is very important. Bacteria from the lower bowel can be harmful in the vagina, causing vaginitis and urinary tract infections. Anything that has been in the rectum—whether finger, penis, or toy—must be cleaned before going into the vagina.

The problem with some of the modern equipment is that it seems to break down just when you need it most or are beginning to enjoy it. You can imagine your frustration when, just at the point of orgasm, the gizmo you have been relying on suddenly stops functioning! The wiring of some of the vibrators seems particularly fragile, and being handy as an electrician may seem almost as important as being a technically efficient lover. *Consumer Reports* has not done a product survey on sexual toys yet, and because of consumers' reluctance to complain, some of the equipment is shoddy and poorly made, breaking the first time you use it. And some of it does not do what it is supposed to do. Yet in spite of the mechanical inconvenience, sexual gadgets can be helpful and fun.

Scott and Sheila found that sexual aids solved a problem for them, making possible a sexual passion they thought had ended. Scott and Sheila had been married three years when a drunk driver hit their car, injuring Scott's spine and paralyzing him from the neck down. This tragedy almost destroyed their lives, their marriage. It created enormous pain and required physical as well as emotional adjustments. Several years passed before their lives were more than dusk-to-dawn drudgery. They had made the changes necessary in order to have a sense of quality and joy in their life. At first they thought their sexual relationship was permanently over. Scott was impotent. Sheila was afraid to bring up the subject of sex, as it might revive his depression about his condition. Luckily, Scott's social worker at the hospital brought up the subject, suggesting several books and new methods of being sexual.

Scott wanted to satisfy Sheila again. He did not want his condition to force her to give up such an important part of life, such a special part of their relationship. He was able to satisfy her through oral-genital contact. He also discovered that he could use a vibrator. Some were lightweight enough to manage even with hands weakened by quadriparesis. He ordered a dildo which would fit over his penis and could be strapped on. They found they could get better body motion with the use of a water bed, the motion of the mattress giving Scott more body movement during intercourse. The closeness, the fusion of their feelings expressed by sex, had been made possible again.

But that was only half the story. Scott was relieved to learn that he could transfer the sexual feelings that had been focused on his genitals to another part of his body. He found it especially exciting when his neck was touched. This was the lowest part of his body where there was still feeling, and it seemed particularly sensitive. They discovered that lotions heightened Scott's pleasure. Some lotions made his flesh feel hot, and some created this feeling when Sheila blew on his skin. He loved it when she kissed and lapped his shoulders, his neck; it was as if all his sensations were there, his whole body encased by her lips. His fantasies were as active as ever. He loved making love with the lights on, using mirrors so that he could see every aspect of Sheila's responsiveness. With Sheila's caressing, his fantasies, and his empathy for her, he felt as if he had an orgasm. He amplified all the sensations that he did have, and the power of his fantasies pushed him to ever longer and more pleasurable ecstasy, so that he had developed an ability to have a mental orgasm. They discovered ways to be sexual again; emotionally they felt closer than ever, understanding things few people had ever even imagined. They had a special sexual relationship, made even more pleasurable with the use of lotions and gadgets.

You and your lover will find your own unique ways of incorporating sexual equipment into your sexual relationship. Perhaps you'd find it a titillating experience simply browsing through a catalogue together, imagining how you could use all these new gadgets. You can buy them as presents for each other or decide to try out your new toy to see how it feels. Clearly a new sexual toy automatically adds variety to your sexual interlude. Some sexual toys you will love and find that you use often. Maybe you will find one that helps resolve a difficulty existing between you. Others may feel the toy gives too much stimulation or feels so mechanical as to be awkward. Below is an alphabetical list of sexual gadgets and lotions, with some suggestions on how a couple can use this equipment.

ARTIFICIAL VAGINA. Artificial vaginas are essentially aids for male masturbation. Portnoy used liver as an organic artificial vagina. The blow-up doll with vaginal and oral receptacles is another form. There are also vibrating sleeves, which fit over the glans of the penis and stimulate this sensitive part. You may enjoy having your spouse watch you masturbate with this.

BEN WA BALL. This is a Chinese device that women have used for centuries. Two rounded forms—either ball- or egg-shaped—are inserted in the vagina, which then reacts sensually to rocking and walking. Sometimes the balls are metal; there is a theory that the colder metal produces "shocks" to the vagina, which thus exercises the PC muscle.

Modern technology has prompted some manufacturers to add a vibrator to the ben wa ball; you don't even need to walk or rock, just turn on the switch. Couples can insert a vibrating ball into the vagina or anus during intercourse.

BODY PAINT. This is truly right out of your children's toy set—the modern adult version of fingerpainting, popularized by the movie *Cousin, Cousine.* Use your fingers to spread colors on your lover's body—perhaps you'd like to paint daisies on your wife's nipples or a bull's-eye on your husband's penis. It is less messy if you do this while you are in the tub together and can then wash it all away in a sensuous spray. You can buy kits called *Body Paints for Lovers* or simply use the soap paint marketed to entice children into taking baths.

CANDY PANTY. Candy panties are exactly what the name implies: ladies' panties made out of a sweet, edible material. They give you something sweet to eat while tickling, licking, and nuzzling your spouse. Candy panties can add a new sensation to oral play and oral-genital sex.

CLITORAL STIMULATOR. This is an ancient method of adorning the penis in such a way as to stimulate the clitoris. A ring goes over the shaft to the base of the penis and has an extension on it that rubs the clitoris during intercourse. It may be helpful for those who need more clitoral stimulation during intercourse in order to reach orgasm. Needless to say, this, too, has been touched by technology—you can buy one with a vibrator. The small vibrating unit rubs your wife's clitoris while the ring attaches to your penis and turns it into a vibrator.

CLOVE SOAP. You can also use this in a couple bath. It smells like cloves and imparts a glow of warmth to the skin. It is a way to add to the couple shower and make it unique.

DILDOS. Dildos are ersatz penises. You can use a natural one, such as a carrot or zucchini, or a plastic one (they come in a wide assortment of lengths and widths). They also come with a double head. One of the most popular vibrators is a battery-operated dildo. The batteries fit inside the dildo, which makes it shake or throb. Some have two speed choices. The dildo vibrators come in a wide variety of sizes from four to ten inches long. They also come in a variety of phallic shapes, some smooth, some with ribs or nubs on the shaft. Some have protrusions so that your vagina and clitoris are vibrated simultaneously. You can also buy sleeves with ridges, bumps, and extensions that fit over the shaft and add different sensations—a French tickler for your vibrator!

For you as a couple, dildos can be used in several different ways. They can stimulate the clitoris with their vibrations; they can be inserted in the vagina or anus. Perhaps you would like to watch your wife masturbate with one, or perhaps you would like to make love with a small one inserted in your anus.

You can buy a hollow dildo, which can be used as a prosthetic penis. This was the way Scott and Sheila were able to have intercourse again. With these, you insert your penis into the dildo and use a harness to attach it to your body. The attached dildo with your penis inside can penetrate your spouse while your body moves in the motions of intercourse. These, too, come in various sizes; some have a vibrator attached, which increases sensation for both of you. They are especially designed for you men who are unable to maintain an erection and wish to please your spouse through intercourse or for women who would like to do some sexual role reversals.

FEATHERS. Feathers can be used in foreplay to provide an extremely delicate touch. They tickle, caress lightly, tease. Use a feather to apply an edible powder, such as a dust made of honey and confectioners sugar, then lick it off.

FINGER SLEEVES. Finger sleeves are decorated latex sleeves that fit over your finger, adding length or width. They originated in Japan and are used in vaginal and anal play, especially with fingers in the vagina and thumb in the anus.

FRENCH TICKLER. These are essentially ornamented condoms. They fit over the penis and come in a wide assortment of decorations. Some add bumps, nobs, or ridges on the shaft of the penis or extensions on the top. The decorations are supposed to heighten sensation for the woman and often increase the length or width of the penis. Some of them are formed like cartoon characters, such as Mickey Mouse, to add humor to the sexual encounter (then you can say you have finally made it as a Mouseketeer).

FUR. Fur can be used like feathers to yield a gentle, soft touch. Dangle a piece of fur over your lover's body, letting it barely touch the flesh. Wrap your hand in the fur, gently stroking your spouse. You may wish to buy a rabbit-fur mitten, which houses a thin vibrator and provides sensuous caresses.

G-SPOTTER. This is an attachment to a wand massager that is designed to be inserted in the vagina and vibrate the G-spot.

ICE. Ice can be used to impart a different sensation to the skin. It causes a definite shock, and you may enjoy the feel of it on your body or on the soles of your feet. You may also wish to try the ice-bag trick. In this the woman places an ice bag on her lover's back—or if you're really daring, on his testicles—right before orgasm. It is supposed to increase the power of the orgasm. Don't do this as a surprise for your lover, as he may really dislike it.

LOTION. There is truly an amazing variety of lotions. All are massage lotions designed to heighten the pleasure in foreplay as you stroke, touch, and lick each other. Some use pheromones or musk scents, so your sense of smell increases your arousal. Others are marketed with food flavors—like strawberry or amaretto—to appeal to your sense of taste. Stimulating lotions impart a sense of warmth to the skin when applied, or need to be blown on or licked to create that sense of hotness. The Kama Sutra collection has the added advantage of coming in sensuous, subtly erotic bottles, so you can imagine your phial contains a genie from the Arabian nights. This makes even opening up the lotion an adventure.

Because there is such a wide variety of lotions, there is a wide variety of uses. Perhaps using a scented lotion as a massage cream would provide a close, quiet evening for the two of you; a sensual massage with a lotion may be extremely helpful in providing a transition from the tension of work to the closeness of intimacy. Using a lotion that adds a warm glow would be a new way to enjoy your lover's body—feeling the warmth tingle and enjoying the new luscious smell.

LUBRICATING GEL. Modern lubricating gels are a vast improvement over the traditional Vaseline and K-Y jelly. They provide excellent lubrication with less goop, creating more slide with less mess. They are water soluble, which means they wash off easily and thus do not harbor bacteria. Some are flavored so that they add a different taste to oral-genital contact, and some are tasteless and odorless, so that you experience your lover's body au naturel. Either is preferable to a mouth full of Vaseline.

There are times when a good lubricating gel may be helpful—such as during pregnancy, after childbirth, during breast-feeding, and after menopause, when the vaginal surfaces are drier. A lubricating gel may also be useful with sexual aids or with condoms.

MASSAGER. There are a number of different massagers made out of wood for body massage. Some are designed to roll on your lover's back or feet, These can be fun when the two of you are massaging each other.

Electric massagers—the "Swedish massager" variety—can add to a full body massage. You can buy them in any department store as body massagers. These have small mounted motors, which are held on the hand with coils. They turn your hand into a vibrating unit, adding oomph to a body massage. They can also be used for genital massage. Since your fingers are touching your lover, you can feel your lover's body and know what spot you are touching and the amount of pressure you are using. This is not true for vibrators and thus makes the massager ideal for couple hand play and foreplay. Unfortunately the hand massager gets heavy after a while, and the coils can catch or pull pubic hair.

NUMBING LOTION. Numbing lotions are a special variety of emollients that numb the skin. They are helpful in preventing premature ejaculation by decreasing feeling in the penis.

PENIS RING. The purpose of a penis ring is twofold—to maintain erection and to create the feeling of a thicker or longer penis. The rings fit over the shaft of the penis and are tight enough to prevent the blood in the erect penis from subsiding, thus helping it to stay erect. Some are also ribbed or nubbed to increase sensation for the woman partner. These are similar to the clitoral stimulator, except the primary purpose is to enhance penile function.

SHOWER MASSAGER. A shower massager is another way to add excitement to the couple shower. These can come with pulsating heads that push water out with rhythmical force. In the shower they can give a different sensation when you wash your spouse's back—they can also be used on the genitals to create even more arousal.

STRING OF PEARLS. String of pearls is a cord with beads or knots on it. It is inserted in the man's anus and just prior to and during climax is pulled out. The beads or knots rub the prostate gland and this added massage intensifies orgasm. Do not reuse the string of beads. The cord cannot be sufficiently cleaned to guarantee that it is not harboring germs.

VAGETTE. The purpose of the Vagette is to restore the tonicity of the PC muscle, which is the muscle that contracts during orgasm and prevents urinary seepage. The Vagette is a new sort of sexual aid, in that it exercises the muscle by applying a small, intermittent electrical current. Its purpose is not to give you pleasure, but to help you respond when you are having sex. It can be ordered from Myodynamics, Inc., 1129-F Dominquez Street, Carson, CA 90746.

VIBRATORS. Vibrators are the most popular and best known of the modern sex gadgets. Many of the ancient sexual paraphernalia—such as dildos and ben wa balls—have been modernized with a vibrating unit. There are three additional sorts of vibrators, all essentially designed to help women achieve orgasm. The wand-type vibrator is a thick, electrically operated machine with a rounded vibrating head. It is excellent for clitoral massage and you can purchase additional attachments that can be inserted in your vagina. There are also gun-shaped vibrators with various attachments that can either be used directly on the scalp, clitoris, vagina, anus, and breast or can be fitted over the penis. These are also electric. The third type is a small vibrator that fits over the clitoris and has straps that fit over the thighs. You can wear this and have complete freedom of movement.

Vibrators are all essentially designed for masturbation. They have been extremely useful in helping women achieve orgasm but have numerous couple uses, too. They may be difficult for you to use on your lover because you can't feel where you are or how much pressure you are using. You may have to give precise instructions to your partner so he knows exactly where to place the vibrator. You may sound as if you are giving directions to him while he is scratching an itch on your back: "A little to the left, up more . . . just a smidgen down . . . softer . . . ah . . . right there. That's it. . . ." Perhaps you would like your lover to watch while you use one, or the two of you can take turns and describe how it feels.

A vibrator may help you become orgasmic during masturbation. For women who want extra clitoral stimulation during intercourse, a vibrator held near the clitoris may be helpful. This is easily accomplished when the woman is sitting on top of the man. The woman can also hold the vibrator on her clitoris when the man enters her from the rear, or when he is on his side and she is on her back, her legs thrown over his hips. You can use the vibrator to teach you how to become orgasmic during intercourse. Then, over a period of time, you can use the vibrator less and less until you have trained yourself to be orgasmic during intercourse without the vibrator.

VINEGAR. A vinegar douche tightens the vagina, creating a tighter fit for the penis.

WATER BED. The water bed gives the feeling of more motion with less effort. You both may feel as if you are rocking together. However, some couples complain that there is less leverage.

WESSON OIL. Wesson Oil—or any cold-pressed vegetable oil—is an inexpensive body lubricant. After a Wesson Oil bath, the two of you can slide and glide over each other and into a greater variety of positions.

WHIPPED CREAM. Whipped cream, like chocolate syrup and honey, is an excellent edible, making oral play fun. Whipped cream sprayed out of a can has an added advantage—you can spray designs on your lover's body. Then you have the delicious joy of licking your artwork off!

Gadgets and gizmos add novelty to your sexual relationship. Lotions and jells change and enhance the sensual experience you share. Vibrators or other gadgets may help you solve a specific sexual difficulty. Sexual paraphernalia, be it ancient or modern, are toys for the two of you to play with together. To explore. To discover. To reinvent. To enjoy.

6

HOME PORNO

It was Mother's Day; the family had taken Monique out for dinner at a nice restaurant, each trying to make her day special. The children had presented their hand-made cards gaily decorated with crayoned rainbows and flowers. Monique teared up at their tender expressions of love for her. Michael gave her a bouquet of tulips but winked and whispered that she had another present coming later. After the kids were tucked in for the night, she ripped open his wrapped and beribboned present. He had bought an 8 mm movie called *Game Time* at the porno store. Monique felt curious, shy, and aroused. "The leading lady," teased Michael, "looks a little like you," and he moved to get their projector out of the closet. Monique giggled, embarrassed, but was eager to explore her feelings and see Michael's reaction. They lay back in bed to watch the movie.

Monique had seen porno before; they had gone to see *Deep Throat* with some friends when it was all the rage. They had both felt a little awkward walking into a porno movie house but were bolstered by their friends and the fact that watching *Deep Throat* was the "in" thing to do—a chic excuse for satisfying their curiosity. It had seemed like a group experience, four couples out for an evening at the movies. At first she was shocked at how the sex looked. It seemed so raw, so animal, so strange. Sex looked different from the way she had imagined it, from the way it felt. The screen images varied from the images she had in her head about sex. But as she watched, she became accustomed to these new images, intrigued. Yet she did not feel excited while watching the movie. Later that night, when she and Michael made love, they discovered she was more responsive than usual, more quickly aroused, and more ardent. For months after that she would recall the images from the movie and these became arousing to her. She found herself using the images and events in her fantasies and was more excited about the idea of sucking Michael's penis than she had been before.

Seeing a XXX-rated movie with Michael in their bedroom was bound to be a different experience. The plot was so simple it was stupid, a seduction scene on a fur blanket in front of a fire. Cozy, but without the Hollywood music and professionalism to give it a glow. But when they were both nude, the Hollywood fade-out was absent and Monique saw the man's erect penis glisten in the firelight. The woman moaned a response to his touches. Monique found herself freer to empathize with the woman on the screen. Michael gently caressed her while they watched. She was becoming aroused. Then the couple in the movie acted out a position that she and Michael had never tried. The man was kneeling on the floor entering the woman, who was on a low platform. Their lovemaking seemed almost tender. How come they had never done that? Boy, did that look like fun! Monique could see the man's penis sliding in and out of the woman's vagina, moving faster and faster. The position looked like it could hold new thrills, and Monique said, "Let's do that! That looks great."

The movie ended and Monique and Michael tried out the position shown to them in the movie. They had learned a new sexual trick. Monique teased Michael about buying her an "educational" game on Mother's Day. She was surprised that she had found watching the movie couple have sex so exciting. Yet Monique had been aroused by the torrid love scenes in *The Postman Always Rings Twice*, *Body Heat*, and some other Hollywood movies. She had also been aroused by reading sexual material—she had started with *Battle Cry*, when it was the most talked about book among her high school friends, then had moved on to the more literary *Lady Chatterley's Lover* and *Tropic of Capricorn.* So, in fact, Monique had always been excited by erotic visual images; now she was comfortable with more explicit visual material, too. Monique still felt too shy and embarrassed to walk into a porno store, but from that Mother's Day on, Michael bought porno movies for presents; and once or twice a year they would enjoy watching them.

Feeling Comfortable With Sexual Images

You, too, may wish to become more comfortable with visual sexual images. You may find yourself becoming aroused when you read erotic passages in books or watch romantic love scenes in movies. Maybe you try to block these feelings, ashamed that you are excited by such material. Yet most of us become excited by reading sexy material and watching erotic scenes. That is why romantic movies and books are so popular. We empathize with the feelings of the characters—reliving a similar scene from our own life or wishing we were the characters on the screen. Such images broaden our sexual vocabulary, help us get in touch with our feelings, and may even teach us new things to do.

Once you accept that you will feel aroused by erotic material, you can decide if you wish to allow yourself the pleasure of more frankly explicit literature and visuals. First, you must decide if it is okay for you to feel aroused by seeing pictures of people performing sexually. There may be many reasons why you have difficulty enjoying explicit sexual material. Perhaps it goes against your upbringing. You may feel that "nice girls" wouldn't be caught dead watching dirty movies. Your mother may be aghast at such a display of your sexuality. "Why, it's worse than sitting with your legs spread!" she might say. If you have incorporated this attitude, you may feel guilty or "slutty" if you watch hard-core porno. Your religious training may also inhibit you. If you feel you will writhe in hell for all eternity, the cost may not be worth the gain. You need to sort out these feelings.

You may also have feelings of squeamishness philosophically, since being turned on by sexual images is counter to the ideology of some sectors of the women's movement. Recently, part of the feminist movement has stated that pornography is always exploitative of women, since it treats them as sexual objects, thereby reinforcing our society's propensity for treating women as sexual objects. This position evolved as an outcry against pornography that portrays women being tortured and raped; the combination of sex and violence was so disgusting that it hardened that sector's political stand against all pornography. Another part of the women's movement is against all forms of censorship; still other women feel that pornography may be sexually liberating for women. You may need to think this issue out for yourself and decide if nonviolent, nonsadistic images of adults making love are politically and morally acceptable to you.

For you women, the whole idea of visual sexual images may be foreign territory. Take it one step at a time, letting yourself become comfortable first with written material, then with increasingly frank visual material. You may feel more comfortable being aroused by written material. Reading books creates an aura of privacy. Reading is safe, secret. It is the domain of women, and an entire section of the publishing industry is devoted to satisfying the romantic and erotic interests of women. So you, like so many other women, may feel swept away by dreamy arousal when you read romantic novels. You may imagine yourself in the role of the heroine and you may fantasize about making love with the male lead. Maybe when you read erotic passages in novels, you feel the tingling sensations of arousal and find your panties damp. In fact, you may especially enjoy an erotic love scene, reading it over and over because of the strong feelings of excitement it provokes. Perhaps you read as part of your foreplay to masturbation. No one knows what you're reading, or why. No one can see the images in your mind and sense how excited you are. You are maintaining the image of a literary or escapist reader. No one knows you are excited by the sexy scenes in *Princess Daisy.* You could be merely engrossed in the fast-paced plot. You can even fool yourself, if you want.

WRITTEN MATERIAL. Iris and Ivan developed a new version of the bedtime story. Iris had always been aroused by reading sexy material. She had worn out a copy of *Peyton Place* as a teenager. In fact, she had first learned to masturbate after reading a passionate scene—she had rubbed her clitoris and labia to relieve that feeling of swollen pressure. She was surprised when she orgasmed and thereafter would reread that particular passage and then touch herself. Ivan also had grown up reading sexual material—his parents' library of marriage manuals. Initially, he'd read them to learn what he was supposed to do, to quash his own anxiety about what exactly happened during sex, and to discover what was most pleasurable. He found himself becoming aroused by the clinical descriptions of positions and foreplay as he empathized with the male.

When *The Joy of Sex* came out, Ivan bought a copy to show to Iris. He was trying to recreate his adolescent excitement and unknowingly tapped into Iris's adolescent excitement, too. As they read the passages, they found themselves becoming increasingly excited. They wanted to try everything that the book talked about that night!

Later, they incorporated reading aloud to each other as part of their foreplay. They took turns reading an erotic scene from a novel. Both of them became aroused. Sometimes they would act out the scene they had just read, and sometimes they acted on the feelings of excitement stimulated by the words. They shared a secret part of their adolescent sexuality with each other in an adult way. It became a cherished component of their sexual relationship—a way to share something special, a way to be uniquely close and sexual. They always remarked how amazing it was that even before they met each other they were sexually following a similar path, as though each were preparing for the other.

You, too, can share written material. Many of you may have used sexy passages in books as a way to heighten your arousal prior to masturbation. Because of your familiarity with written material—be it hard-core porno or literary masterpieces—you may feel less vulnerable sharing this with your mate. Let your lover know what books turn you on. Perhaps your lover would like to read this material, too, to learn something about you. Some of you may enjoy the old-fashioned practice of reading books out loud to each other, maybe you take turns dramatically reading a murder mystery or a science-fiction story. You can add a new twist to this hobby by reading sexually explicit material. The two of you can get in bed together and take turns reading to each other, or maybe you would prefer lying side by side reading silently. You may use the sexual feelings to increase your passion or you can use reading as part of foreplay.

VISUAL MATERIAL. Looking at a picture of naked people or people making love necessitates an open acceptance and definition of you as a sexual, lusty person. Your immediate reaction may be that you are not excited by seeing erotic images. Additionally, you may believe that only men are aroused by the sight of nude or partially clad women but that nude males are not a turn-on. You may feel that this area of sexuality is the province of men. Stop and think a minute. Do any visual images arouse you? Maybe it's the vague romantic scenes in standard movies, prime-time TV, or soap operas that create feelings of warmth in your crotch and give your sexual imagination more material. Maybe it's the sexy man with hair curling over his open shirt in a cigarette commercial or scenes of John Travolta dancing and flexing his muscles.

You may respond to these images, and if you do, then visual images do excite you. And these images can serve as a bridge to more explicit material. The next step is to test your reaction to more frank and obvious material. Again, your head may be arguing that women are not aroused by explicit sexual material, but only by romantic images. The rapid gain in popularity of male strippers belies that notion. Research also indicates that women do become aroused when watching pornography but may not admit this even to themselves. If you own your sexuality, you will probably find that visual material excites you. Most of us are aroused by movies. Although men seem to be especially turned on by visual stimulation, both males and females are aroused by pornographic films. Men are especially excited by films depicting group sex and lesbian activity, while the greatest magnitude of physical arousal for women occurs watching group sex and heterosexual activity.

If you wish to become comfortable with visual material, try still photos first. Pictures and sculptures of naked people are beautiful, the nude human body is a joy to behold, the finest, most advanced product of evolution. Erotic art books can be purchased at any fine bookstore. Almost every art style from Japanese woodcuts to Picasso has produced some erotic art. Some depictions are very beautiful, romantic, tender, or lusty. Others are whimsical or funny. Erotic art may help you become comfortable with frank pictures of people being sexual together. Photographs of people making love vary from the sublime to the raw.

VISUAL PORNOGRAPHY. Visual pornography is any image whose sole purpose is to create a feeling of arousal or excitement. There is "soft-core" pornography, which does not show erect male sexual organs, and hard-core pornography, which does show sexual organs, erection, and ejaculation. There are close-ups of the sexual organs performing sexual acts. There is generally little attempt to romanticize the subject matter or to show any relationship other than a sexual one between the actors. The humanity of the characters is minimized, they are almost disembodied sexual organs performing. These images of actual sexual acts from the camera's eye are different from how sex looks to you while you are doing it and are probably different from how you imagine it looks.

Hard-core pornography embraces every imaginable sexual act, and some that you probably never imagined. There is a vast range of material, a veritable circus of sexuality for you to choose from. Some pornography is well done, expressing passion, and some is tawdy and raw, in poor taste. Regardless, your most secret, private fantasies have been acted, photographed, and printed for you to see. Everyone has a favorite sexual fantasy—pornography provides material to fuel that fantasy. You can find heterosexual, homosexual, and lesbian couples. You may see three, four, or more people entwined in the gymnastic variations of group sex. There are images of intercourse, vaginal and anal, and sometimes both of these at the same time. Images of oral-genital sex abound, in all its heterosexual, homosexual, lesbian, and bisexual variations. In addition, there are magazines and movies devoted to bondage and discipline, to "kiddy porn" and to sadism and masochism. Pornography that depicts the drawing of blood or involves an act that has been forced on someone is not helpful for promoting loving or passionate feelings between long-term mates.

The human body is beautiful and the sexual organs joining and moving together are beautiful. Yet picking out the good from the bad, the tasteful from the disgusting, the sensitive from the unappetizing, can feel overwhelming. An easy approach is to look at these images slowly, starting with the most romantic and familiar, then moving on to the more exotic. What is your response to the image before you? If your reaction is disgust, put it away. Possibly you feel bored. Test if this is your true feeling when you make love that night. If you find yourself more passionate than usual, then your feeling of boredom is a screen that your unconscious is using. You have not truly accepted that it's okay for you to be aroused by this material. Imagining yourself in one of the roles may help you get in touch with your physical responses and accept that the images are arousing to you.

Now you're ready for movies. Obviously there may be some images in the movies that are not exciting to you. Maybe you find yourself turned on by watching two men kissing, but not two women. Perhaps you are excited by images of intercourse but blasé during the episodes of oral-genital contact. Most pornographic material is not made to arouse women. For example, in many pornographic movies the man withdraws his penis from the women to ejaculate outside of her body. This is so the mostly male audience will empathize with his pleasure. However, for many women this may be anticlimactic. On the other hand, you may allow yourself to feel much excitement by the screen lovers. You may find yourself wishing that your spouse did a particular thing portrayed on the screen to you. You may find the image of another woman's body or the idea of two men pleasuring you thrilling. What is arousing to you may surprise you, may teach you new things about your sexuality, and may give you new ideas of sexual variations with your spouse.

For you men, the idea of visual images being arousing is not new. You probably have grown up with the airbrushed ideal of the woman's body as depicted in the pinup calendar or magazine. Perhaps you masturbated to these pictures, imagining your body close to the woman's in the picture. You have been conditioned to believe that the sight of the female body is arousing. You may have seen XXX-rated movies with your friends and perused magazines of photos with people making love. You are probably more comfortable with this area of sexuality than your spouse. Your difficulty may be in sharing this area of yourself with her. It may represent your adolescent frustrations and inadequacy to you, or it may feel private. You may be concerned that she would be disappointed at the idea of you masturbating to a picture. If you are going to enjoy sexual material together, you need to share this with her, to let her know which images are arousing to you and how a certain book or a certain model's body became part of your sexual vocabulary.

Home-Grown Home Porno

MAKING IT YOURSELF. There are many ways to weave pornography into the fabric of your sexual relationship. Perhaps the best way is by making it yourself. In this case you have the double pleasure of seeing you and your lover together and seeing an erotic image. You can't help but empathize with your own pleasure. If you catch an image of you and your spouse making love, you can inadvertently make your own porno.

This is what happened with Gwen and Gordon. They were making love, the soft glow of a candle on their bedside table sending shadows arching over the walls and ceiling. Gwen suddenly saw one of the shadows moving rhythmically, waving slowly on the wall. At first she didn't know what caused it, but then she realized the waving motion was Gordon's back. He pressed his buttocks into her and part of the shadow moved, while the large hump representing his shoulders and their heads rocked slowly. She was fascinated, seeing their bodies, their lovemaking, thrown into a soft, dark blur echoing them. "Look," she whispered to Gordon, "there are our shadows on the wall making love with us." The two of them turned their heads and watched the shadows move. Slowly the small curve that was Gordon's buttocks moved down, and then the large hump rocked. They melted into one shape, one form, one body. As they went faster and faster, they watched the subtle grays and blues shudder on the wall, the shadows arc together and then dissolve with orgasm.

"That was really beautiful," said Gordon. They both felt strangely moved by the experience—closer, more intimate. Their shadow selves had also joined. After that, they often placed the candle so that their bodies would shine from the wall. The shadows brought their arousal to fever pitch and they realized that the very sight of their bodies moving as reflected by the shadows had become exciting. They liked watching themselves make love, so it wasn't too long before one of them realized the tremendous possibilities inherent in mirrors. They had a large dresser mirror, which they placed on a chair beside the bed. They could see their bodies stretched out next to each other. Gwen could see Gordon bend down to kiss her abdomen, see his head become lost between her legs. When he entered her, they watched their bodies move together, but this time the blurred, gray shadowy forms had altered to the crispness of fleshtones. They could see the clear demarcation of Gordon's body from Gwen's. He could see her hips and waist move as she rocked on her back, and she could see the clenching of his buttocks. They looked beautiful, moving together in this ancient dance.

1. MIRRORS. Like Gwen and Gordon, you can make your own erotic images. Mirrors strategically placed around your bed can reflect different aspects of your bodies as you make love. You can see and feel and see yourself feeling at the same time. You can see your lover's body, your lover's responses, your lover's arousal, your lover touching you. You may enjoy watching your own prowess and exhibiting for the two of you your ability to incite passion. The mirrors may appeal to the exhibitionist in you or to the voyeur—all in the safety of your couplehood, your intimacy. You may enjoy watching some parts of your lovemaking, but not others. Perhaps you enjoy foreplay but find watching intercourse distracting.

Maybe you need to be very aroused and close to orgasm before seeing your passion is exciting. With mirrors you can watch yourselves, see what the motions of sex look like.

2. POLAROID. There is no doubt that the Polaroid camera has added greatly to a couple's collection of sexy pictures. This is one step removed from the immediacy of the mirrors but gives you an image of each other. You can take pictures of each other. Some of these can be naked, some can be like the centerfolds in the magazines—from demure to frank open-leg pictures showing the folds of the vulva and erect penis. If you have a tripod and timer, you can set your photographic equipment up so that you can have a picture of the two of you having sex in various positions. Setting up the equipment, getting into a position, hearing the click of the lens, and starting the whole process over again may not feel romantic to you but may feel like sexy fun. An automatic reset will take pictures at intervals for you and give you a set of stills in a time sequence. Seeing the photographs may be arousing and might satisfy some curiosities you may have.

3. VIDEO CAMERA. From the Polaroid to the movie camera or video recorder takes only a small step in imagination. If you have enjoyed looking at the still pictures of yourselves or watching you and your lover in mirrors, you may also enjoy a home movie. Again, you'll need a tripod and a camera. This time you'll be able to lose yourselves to your feelings while the camera hums along recording your movements. Then you will have made your own porno movie and can see you and your mate being sexual together. Mirrors, still photos, and movies are all ways you and your lover can be hero and heroine in a sexually explicit visual episode.

HIGH-TECH VISUALS. Candy felt abandoned again. She and Crosby had just made love. It seemed satisfying to both of them, the smell of their sexual union still hung in the air. But Candy could see the gray glow from the TV in the next room and knew that Crosby was in there watching TV. At first that had not bothered her, though she was concerned by his insomnia. But one night she went in to see if he was okay and he was watching the porno movies on cable TV. Somehow she felt jealous, scared, as though she weren't enough for him. He was watching all those naked women prancing across the screen, watching those other couples make love. Perhaps he thought those other women had more beautiful breasts or trimmer waists. They probably didn't have stretch marks on their stomachs from their last pregnancy or a smattering of gray hair. She felt inadequate, as though she weren't sexy or attractive enough for him, as though she hadn't really satisfied him. If he was still interested in sex, she'd be glad to make love again. Why was he watching those damn movies?

Finally, Candy decided to ask him. He didn't seem the least bit ashamed or embarrassed by her knowing that he watched the movies. Crosby explained that they were arousing to him, and he liked that feeling. He had grown up in a rural environment and had worked very hard as a teenager and young man. He felt he had missed out on the sexual revolution, and that this was one way to satisfy his curiosity about other women, about what other people did sexually. He did not compare the women on TV to her; she was real and they were fantasy to him. Crosby asked her to watch with him. Candy figured, "If you can't fight 'em, join 'em," and agreed. One night after they made love, Crosby turned on the TV. Candy sat next to him and together they watched the movie. Later they made love again; the movie had acted as a way to rest and become aroused again for more sex. With time she became comfortable watching the movies, and occasionally she would turn on the TV, watch a porno movie, and then make love. Candy experienced arousal, curiosity, and sometimes boredom watching the movie. She came to accept her husband's interest. She no longer felt jealous and inadequate, but rather the porno movie had become a sexual tool for both of them to share.

Watching porno movies in your own home is a different experience from going to a theater. You are alone, not part of an anonymous group. If you are a man, you do not have to be "one of the boys" or portray a "macho" image of casualness regarding your feelings. If you are a woman, you do not have to deal with the embarrassment of being a woman in a porno movie theater or deny any sensations of arousal you feel. You are safe. You are not displaying your sexuality to the world, only to your spouse. Certainly at home a woman can feel secure and unstained. Like the old saying—"A lady in the living room and a whore in the bedroom"—you are free to be as ladylike and Puritan in public and as wanton and lusty in private as you wish. You both are free to act on your feelings. In your own home, you are free to recognize your feelings. Moreover, you are free to act on your feelings, so that watching a movie in the privacy of your home with your lover may be an erotic experience.

There is a wide range of arousing visual material. Perhaps, for you, *Love Story* and the scene in *Gone With the Wind* in which Rhett Butler carries Scarlett up the staircase are very erotic. Maybe you are also turned on by watching XXX-rated porno. Some of this depends on the movie itself and your response to the images that are portrayed. Porno movies vary greatly. Some are quite raw, and some are funny. Some of the movies are quite gentle, almost romantically done, focusing on the tenderness between the people. There are many different ways you can acquire porno movies in the privacy of your home.

1. CABLE TV. One of the first and one of the most heavily subscribed channels for cable TV has been the porno movie channel. In some areas, this is soft-core pornography, that is, movies that show nudity, but where the sexual joining is pretended and the males do not have erections. In other areas, XXX-rated films are shown. These are movies in which you can see the penetration of the vagina by the penis, and in which the males have erections and ejaculations. In order to have either of these types of movies in your home, you must purchase a special subscription, which costs, in addition to the cable, under $10 per month. Sometimes these channels are marketed under special names, such as Escapade, or Playboy.

2. VIDEOCASSETTE RECORDER. In addition to cable TV, a videocassette recorder can play full-length films. This is a device that can play movies you buy or rent on your TV and can record TV programs for later playback. With a camera you can make your own home videos and play them on your TV. This equipment is expensive, and the individual movie cassettes sell for under $50. You can also rent a movie or join a rental club. The feature-length porno

movie is much more technically advanced than *Deep Throat*. Many of you who would be too embarrassed to go to a porno movie enjoy watching *Debbie Does Dallas* or *Blazing Zippers*. Fourteen percent—or $150 million—of home video revenue comes from adult videos. It is obvious that many people are enjoying porno movies in the privacy of their home. Video porn is rapidly becoming respectable. Additionally, Universal Pictures is making a series of sex education films entitled *Love Skills*.

3. PORNO BOOKSTORE. The third source for porno movies is the porno bookstore. For a woman, the porno bookstore is, perhaps, the most difficult place to enter. Cable TV and video stores are retail outlets that sell a wide variety of goods. Walking in one does not announce that you are there to buy sexual material. This is not true of the porno bookstore; it sells only sexually explicit material and aids.

In spite of this and her own reluctance, Monique wanted to buy Michael a porno magazine. She decided to visit the local porno bookstore, which was located in the most run-down section of town. Standing outside, Monique noted how seedy it looked. The storefront displayed some of the merchandise; the covers of the books were dusty and faded by time. A sign on the door loudly proclaimed, "No one under 18 allowed." She took a deep breath and walked inside. Against the walls were racks of magazines, with signs announcing the subject matter: bondage, hetero, homo, group. Additionally, there were wire racks of books with sexually explicit stories.

In the back were peep shows. Monique went into a private booth, which had a small viewer containing a movie only she could see. When she put her eyes up to the lenses and dropped in a quarter, she could see a flickering movie image of a man and a woman undressing. Just as it got exciting, the movie stopped and she had to drop in another quarter to see what happened next; this happened several times.

The porno bookstore also sold sexual aids. These were mostly the phallic-shaped vibrators, massage lotions, and French ticklers. They also had inflatable rubber dolls, which came equipped with sexual receptacles. Here Monique could also buy an 8 mm or 16 mm film for under $20. The films had dropped in price, the man behind the counter told her, because of stiff competition from the video cassette industry. These films contained one complete episode per reel. She needed a projector and a screen, or a wall, to run these movies. The store also sold movies for a cassette recorder, some of which had never played the theater chains.

At first the porno bookstore truly felt like the domain of men. Even the sexual aids were aimed to appeal to men and male fantasies; there were no vibrators designed primarily for clitoral massage. The young, casually dressed, neatly groomed salesman had not even heard of them. But Monique was relieved to see other women enter the store. Several couples in their midtwenties, looking like college kids, were browsing through the merchandise. Some women were alone, too. During the daytime, about one-third of the customers were women, the salesman told her. When a woman came in alone at night, however, the men assumed she was looking "for something." Monique bought a magazine with photos of a couple making love and a scented massage lotion.

You may use porno movies in several ways. You can learn new ways to express your sexual feelings, new positions to try, and new things to do. Maybe you see a woman stroking her lover's body with a piece of fur and decide to try that. This is an intellectual or educational use of the porno movie. You can use the movie as a way to initiate sex. Maybe you enjoy laughing at the silliness of *Deep Throat* while eating popcorn, getting a kick out of the funny aspects of sexuality. Quietly watching the movie with your lover may lead to kissing and touching each other. Then you may continue to deepen your arousal and make love. You can also decide to make love and watch the movie as part of your foreplay. Maybe you'll mimic the movie characters and follow their lead, doing the same things that they do. Perhaps you will lie close to each other, caressing and fondling, and then be sexual together when the movie is over. Maybe you will watch the movie in between sexual acts. You and your lover will evolve some of your own ways to enjoy sexually explicit movies.

Enjoying pornography with your lover may lead you to explore new horizons. You are stimulating a sexual feast for your eyes, adding visual images to those you already have in your mind.

7

COSTUMES AND SPECIAL EVENTS

Greet your husband in a black see-through baby doll with a drink in one hand, suggests an author teaching you to become a total woman. A little difficult for you to pull off, let alone act on the implicit invitation, when your three-year-old is clinging to your leg and pulling on the lace hem of your lingerie. Yet there is certainly a time for dressing up and playing pretend. This is another way to add an element of play to your relationship, to heighten the seduction. These activities range from sexual clothing to a strip tease.

CLOTHING. Clothing has long been used to lure sexual attentions. Human beings born without the colorful plumage of the peacock or the vivid coloration of the sexual organs of the baboon have compensated by using decoration to focus sexual attention on specific areas. Any of your clothing can become sexual attire if it feels sensual and arousing to you, the wearer, or if it heightens sexual interest for the viewer. Yet many of you may disregard this aspect of sexual interaction. Your ordinary underwear and nightclothes may well be one of the most neglected areas of your wardrobe. In the first flush of your sexual relationship you may have used panties and bras to enhance sexuality in the foreplay stage. You may have thought about the romantic image you would create when you bought nightclothes for your trousseau. You may have bought bikini shorts in your wife's favorite colors. Now your purchases may well be geared to the practical rather than the romantic. You may buy a warm nightgown that covers you from neck to wrist to ankles so that in the morning you can cook breakfast for your children in it or comfort a crying toddler in the middle of the night. You may wear faded flannel pajamas. You may have for so long shopped with an eye to the practical that you are unaware of the vast assortment of underwear and lingerie available now—some of it seductive and more practical than you have imagined.

In our modern civilization we are offered a smorgasbord of styles, colors, and fabrics to choose from. There has been an entire new line of fashion dedicated to leisure activities, from workout clothes, to blue jeans, to "at home" attire. At-home attire is designed so that you can look attractive for your lover while feeling comfortable and sensual yourself. The range is tremendous—long, flowing gowns, see-through negligees, soft velour robes, satiny smoking jackets, and much more.

A great deal of the clothing seems designed to appeal to your sense of touch. Your flesh feels the new sensation, your fingers can enjoy the experience of a different skin. Particularly with the discovery of polyester, which feels like silk, and with synthetic suedes and leathers, there is a wide range of sensual feelings available in fabrics. The manufacturers of clothing are aware that you purchase articles partially because of how they feel on your body, and they thus appeal to the idea that feeling your clothes while you wear them can be a sensual experience. Soft fabrics slide over your body and caress you as you move. Silky nightgowns and pajamas may feel sensual brushing against you and sound elegant as they swish around your legs as you walk. Fur and velour may make you feel like a tiger on the prowl or a shy fox. Even sweatpants and sweatshirts create a warm, soft sensation on your body. You may wear an angora sweater to turn you into a fuzzy bunny, while a nubby, fuzzy fabric may make you feel like a large, cuddly teddy bear. Your wife may love to feel your arms and shoulders under the softness of velour. Leather and suede also feel good on the skin, smooth, responding to the warmth of your body, smelling fresh and raw.

Some clothing is designed for specific sexual visual appeal. There is sexy lingerie, which you might buy and wear for both sexual and practical purposes, such as a garter belt, strapless or push-up bra, or a slinky, skimpy nightgown that feels comfortable to wear while sleeping. There are teddies, tap pants, and camisoles. There are sleepshirts, baby dolls, and lingerie sets. There are sexy undershorts and sensual pajamas. Most are washable, more practical than you realized, and sexier than you imagined.

There are also types of underwear designed mainly for sexual purposes. There are bras with the nipples cut out; panties with holes in the crotch; G-strings in sequins, feathers, or leather; garter belts to hold up seamed stockings; and corsets that reveal and tease, covering breasts and midriff to just below the crotch. You can buy an entire outfit: black bra, garter belt, crotchless panties, and net stockings, adding black gloves and high heels, if you wish. Leather has long been known for its unique erotic appeal. The smell of leather is fresh and sensual, it glistens and molds to your body, its shininess moves as you move, drawing attention to your motions. And it feels soft; you are truly wearing a different skin. Leather jock straps or pants may be enticing to your lover; or if demure subtlety is your style, try a silky teddy with drawstring neck, slit up to the waist in peek-a-boo white lace.

It is easy to incorporate sexual clothing into your relationship. You know what colors, what areas of your body appeal most to your mate. If he is turned on by your breasts, a push-up or nippleless bra might be exciting. If he loves your buns, perhaps a high-cut teddy or hipless pair of panties would be arousing to both of you. Maybe you would love to see your husband in shiny bikini underwear or shorts printed with kisses or hearts. Buy some of the new underwear. Frederick's of Hollywood has long provided the ultimate catalogue for sexy clothes, but sexy underwear and lingerie is so commonplace that many mail-order houses and department stores now sell skimpy black lace teddies, garter belts, and other lingerie designed for its erotic appeal.

Wear your new underwear, perhaps casually under your jeans and T-shirt. What a surprise when you take off your clothes and he sees your new sexy underwear! Or perhaps you could wear your new clothes the next time you have a bed picnic or play strip poker. Maybe, you would like to greet your lover dressed in sexy clothes when he comes home. In other words, all you have to do is buy it and wear it, casually, as an announcement that you're interested in sex, or as a surprise. You know what would feel most comfortable for you and what would most likely create interest for your mate.

SMELL. Part of dressing up to enhance your erotic appeal can include perfume. It seems that men are especially turned on by visual elements, and women are particularly excited by smell. There is no doubt that smell plays a part in our sexuality, a part that is just beginning to be understood by scientists. Do you know that odor even plays a part in your menstrual cycle? Smelling another woman's body odor will encourage your menstrual cycle to coincide with hers. This is the reason that women who live together often menstruate at the same time. Human beings are the only mammals with special sweat glans in the pubic region. Clearly sexual odors stimulate sexual interest.

The perfume industry has capitalized on this by distilling pheromone, the chemical substance that unconsciously stimulates sexual arousal (there is one "scent" for women and another for men).

Moreover, your own body odor may have become eroticized by your mate. Your lubrication, sweat, and genital odors all signal promises of sexual pleasure and thus augment a sensual environment. Some women have capitalized on this by using their own vaginal lubrication on pulse points as a way of subtly signaling their own sexual interest and luring their lover's response. Be aware of your lover's response to smell. Maybe your wife loves the smell of your armpit after a day's work or a hard run. Maybe a particular after-shave makes her want to nuzzle her head in your chest. Use this information. Wear cologne, or after-shave, or scented soaps, or your own body sweat as an aphrodisiac. Use erotic aromas when you want to appear as seductive and enticing as possible to your mate.

CHANGING YOUR BODY. You can also decorate your own body. This is certainly the primitive way of enhancing sexual attractiveness. Primitive tribes have used scarification and body painting to decorate their bodies, and they enhanced the appearance of the sexual organs themselves with paint, fabric, beads, and tassles. The penis has been a particular focus of adornment—rings of gold and feathers, to which metal and ivory extensions were added, have been used to make a good thing even better.

In our civilization, the head has long received extensive attention: we make up our faces in an array of glistening colors, pierce our lobes for earrings of metal and jewels, and dye our hair. We even undergo surgery on our faces to make us look beautiful and young. Now, however, there seems to be burgeoning interest in body alteration as well. There are exercises to tone and firm your flesh and body gleamers to highlight or add sparkle to your skin. You can rouge your breasts or color your nipples with lipstick. If you wish you can try shaving your pubic hair, which would impart a new look and feel to your genitals.

Perhaps you'd like to focus visual interest by getting a tattoo on your breast, buttock, or thigh. There can be a kind of sexual fascination with a tattoo. A tattoo emphasizes and redefines a specific part of your body. Debbie and Don loved their tattoos and used them as part of their sexual play. Don had a tattoo on his hipbone. When Debbie first saw his dragon, she was fascinated. His flesh was as smooth as it was elsewhere, only colored. It was his body, yet not his body. It moved and stretched, and sometimes almost seemed to yawn. It was a living part of him. Debbie could not take her eyes off it, or his hip. Around the time that they realized they were committed to each other, Debbie decided she wanted a tattoo, also, and after much consideration got a little unicorn on her hip. It felt like a secret sign they both shared and seemed to bring them even closer together, like a wedding ring but private and sexier. Don loved her unicorn and called it her "little pony," caressing it and kissing it, watching it prance when she moved. Best of all, when they made love, the dragon and the unicorn were joined, too.

If a permanent tattoo seems too great a commitment, you can buy kits and paint one on for an evening. The idea is to explore ways to add variety to your sexual life, to dress for it, whether by making up your body, adding a musk perfume, or wearing new sexy lingerie.

DRESS-UP AND HALLOWEEN. Beth and Bert were getting ready for the Halloween party. Beth had not worn a costume since she was in sixth grade—she remembered being Tinkerbell back then. It had been a big thrill, putting on the costume and the makeup, but she'd left that joy behind in adolescence, along with her Barbie dolls and security blanket. Now she found herself looking forward again to the play element of dressing as if she were a different person. She was excited about the mystery of the night. Would her friends recognize her? Would she know who they were? She felt anonymous and carefree.

Bert caught her mood. He decided to go as a wolf, a creature he'd always admired. Covered from head to toe, and disguising his voice in a growl, he felt he was no longer himself. It would be hard to recognize him. He wanted to see if even Beth would know him and suggested they go separately and then see if they could recognize each other. Beth agreed and then decided to go as a clown so she could disguise her face with makeup. They had a great time at the party but had no trouble recognizing each other—Bert's walk and dance movements were so uniquely his that they could not be disguised even by the cumbersome wolf suit, and Beth's tinkling laugh was a giveaway. The game was fun. When they came home they kept their costumes on and tried to stay in their roles—Bert the lone wolf, conning Beth into kisses; Beth the silly clown, laughing and giggling.

Some of you may find dressing up in costumes erotic. The exciting, forbidden element of being someone else—making love not with your mate, but with some new exotic lover—comes into play here. Being someone else may give you permission to be less inhibited, to be freer and more playful about your sexuality.

DANCE. Like clothing, dance is a way to beguile and seduce. You, the long-term couple, can still go out for an evening of dancing, moving your bodies with a familiarity and ease that is absent in a courting couple. And you can find music to your tastes—whether it's an evening of square dancing or waltzing. If you go to the discos, you may be surprised to see the young people twisting the night away just as you did in the early sixties. The vogue for nostalgia can help you feel more at ease, and you can do the jitterbug, Watusi, twist, or jerk and still be pretty much in style, even though you can't do the moon walk and breaking might certainly break you!

There is also private dancing, which the two of you do alone together. You can waltz or fast dance to the music, enjoying your bodies as they move together in a different way; or you can throw tradition to the winds and move out together in a creative modern dance, using the music to express your mood. You can play out imaginary stories, reenact lovemaking, taunt, and tease. How comfortable you are with this will be partially dependent on how much you enjoy dancing and how much dancing was a part of your courtship. Feel your emotions, then express them freely in the way you move your body. Remember, it's just the two of you. Even if you both end up in hysterical laughter about how silly you feel, it's a new physical experience together.

PERFORMANCE DANCING. Perhaps you'd like to entertain your spouse with a dance of your own creation, a dance designed to beguile and seduce. The night when Beth and Bert were in their Halloween costumes was especially good for them. The sex was potent and exciting, and Beth wanted to reexperience that same ardent lust. What would be more romantic and sexy than an Arabian dancer, wearing jewels and yards of scarves. Beth decided to take up belly dancing; she wanted to learn how to move her hips in exotic motions as though she were making love to the air, suggestive, enticing. She loved the lessons and found them excellent exercise. Her increased stamina and strengthened muscles began paying off sexually, and she found that she could move longer without tiring, and move in new ways.

Finally Beth decided it was time for her first private performance. She loved the costume, the scarves draped over her body, clinging yet floating, revealing yet hiding. The exotic music enhanced the fantasy she was creating for herself and Bert. The tempo of the music was designed to repeat the tempo of sex itself, starting off slowly and moving to an ever-increasing beat. At first Bert felt awkward, as if he were the guinea pig in an experiment. Then he was entranced. Beth's rotating hips and waving arms were seductive, soothing yet arousing. He found himself wanting to kiss her stomach, hold her and undress her.

Beth found erotic dancing lots of fun and decided to continue learning. It appealed to the exhibitionist in her, and she liked the idea of Bert watching her as she displayed her wares. She decided she wanted to learn to do a strip and whirl the tassles on pasties. She was surprised at how difficult it was to find any information. The librarian at the local library tried to be helpful, but they had no information, not even Gypsy Rose Lee's autobiography. Unfortunately, a young man who wanted to be a male stripper had checked out all the books on belly dancing, so there wasn't even anything on that. At the bookstore, the salesperson broke out in giggles and they discovered that there hadn't even been a book published on erotic dancing or stripping. It seemed strange to her, since male stripping was becoming so popular.

She was able to get some articles and learn the basic philosophy of stripping. Using pasties was a different problem. Beth had a set of gorgeous red-sequined pasties, which she had bought in New Orleans on vacation with Bert. They looked terrific glued on, too, hiding yet emphasizing her nipples. Her breasts looked beautiful, she decided. Nude, yet not nude. Her unadorned flesh contrasted sharply with the bright, glittering pasties.

Unfortunately she could find no information on how to get them to twirl once they were glued on. They bounced from side to side as she moved her hips. By leaning over and swaying her breasts, she could get the tassles to twirl, but as soon as she stood up they hung still. She discovered that when she moved her arms as if she were jumping rope, the tassles twirled; but that hardly created an exciting image. She realized that it must be the same principle as the hoola hoop—she never could learn that, either. Well, the pasties looked terrific on and could be part of a strip act accompanied with appropriate bumps and grinds. Bert was moved by Beth's strip. It seemed so sensual watching her move in the darkened room. Her familiar body was changed by the costume; he saw the motions he had felt when they were making love being played out before his eyes. There she was, alone, moving to the motions of a phantom lover. It was much more arousing than a burlesque. This was a dance for him—a seduction for his benefit.

Bert decided to join in. He found that he, too, could move to the music, slowly taking off his clothes, making each button he unbuttoned part of his dance. He slowly unzipped his pants, then teased her by rocking his twisted shirt between his legs, as though he were riding a horse. Together they danced, undressing themselves and each other, until at last they lay on the bed naked, laughing, and making love.

You, too, may wish to do erotic dancing. Belly dancing is becoming an increasingly popular recreation, and classes are springing up all over. And it is one form of dancing in which thinness is not the ideal. You may also wish to learn the strip tease. The art of a strip is the same whether the dancer is male or female, although different parts of the body are emphasized. As a female dancer, you may wish to emphasize your breasts with pasties or a sexy bra, your legs with net stockings. As a male dancer, you may wish to highlight your bicep with a bracelet or show off the hair on your chest with a vest or neck chain. Regardless of the costume, the dance is essentially a tease. You—the stripper—almost, but not quite, let the watcher see it all. With each item of clothing shed, you are closer to the nude state so desperately desired by the watcher, who is eager for the next glimpse of flesh.

You hint that the watcher will get it all—your nudity, your sexual organs, your orgasm. You can do this by joking, the Gypsy Rose Lee way. Here it's not what you take off so much as the symbol of your clothing being removed that entices and teases. Eagerness for your nudity can also be enhanced by shadow seeing—using fans or scarves so that your naked body is almost, but never really, seen. If that fan would just move a little more, maybe he could see a nipple. If the scarf would just blow in the breeze, maybe he could see your pubic hair. If those shorts were just a little lower, maybe she could see what was making that bulge. As in all teasing, the frustration of not getting what is wanted increases the desire for it.

Thus your partially clothed body creates desire by increasing the other person's need to see you completely nude.

In addition to the tease of the clothing, you can also tease with the motions you make. You, the dancer, move your body in the motions of intercourse. The two most traditional movements are the "bump" and the "grind." In the bump, you push your hip out to the side in a sudden movement, keeping the rest of your body still. Then you can bump to the other side. In a grind, you rotate your hips, flipping your pubic bone at the front as though grinding it into an imaginary lover. Fantasize that you have an invisible lover, imagine what your lover is doing to you, and pretend you are extremely sexually hot, avid for your lover's touches, eager to take off your clothes and be totally nude for your lover; then move according to what your lover is doing, bumping and grinding, bending and arching, dancing out and exaggerating the motions of sex.

Stripping is something you can practice alone in front of a mirror, using your imagination and a hard thumping music in the background. This is something both of you can do, as male stripping is also erotic and a way for you to surprise your wife. Certainly doing a strip for your spouse is playing at the sexual, teasing and enticing. Set the stage for your performance—soft lights, incense or perfume, bowls of fruit—to help you create the aura you desire. Perhaps your spouse will become aroused by your dance, perhaps your spouse will enjoy the playfulness, the sensuousness of the escapade. In any case you will have added a little spark to your sexual relationship.

8

FANTASIES AND TRUSTS

Sand ripped through her hair, and his arms were around her as they glided over the desert on a camel. Scared, yet secretly thrilled, Rachel rocked in his arms. He was ruggedly handsome, dangerous but tameable. He had captured her and carried her off to a canopied tent. Gently he placed her on his mat and strode out of the tent to handle the affairs of his tribe of Bedouins. She knew that later that night he would claim her as his prize.

"Darling, how would you like to go to a movie tonight?" Robert's voice broke through Rachel's reverie. She had been washing the dishes on automatic pilot, off in a movie of her own. How she wished she could live out some of her fantasies—like making love under the stars, serenaded by the sound of the wind in the leaves. Sometimes she would see a man walking down the street; a man who had a certain dark look about him, who walked with an air of confidence. She would imagine his arms as pillars on either side of her head and her hands on his back. During these romantic daydreams her mind would wander and she would find herself imagining all sorts of sexual acts. She didn't know where these thoughts came from; occasionally she was amazed at the variety and vividness of the images. They were like effervescent pictures that floated over her, then disappeared as quietly as they came; dreams quickly forgotten, almost impossible to retell.

Some of the acts remained highlighted in her mind. Once she imagined kissing another woman, caressing her breasts, nestling her head between her legs. Sometimes she replayed sexual adventures she had already done. She remembered vividly the time she and Robert made love in their backyard one summer night. How exciting it had been when he'd first penetrated her! She had been open and trembling with anticipation, he had been eager to zero in on his home place. Sometimes she imagined a new lover, and sometimes she fantasized about doing new exotic things with Robert—things that she wanted to do but was timid about trying, such as making love in a men's room. Mostly, though, the weight of the fantasy was in the seduction, such as being carried off on a camel and then rescued by an even more dashing figure.

The Role of Sexual Fantasy

All of us have sexual fantasies, images that remind us during the day of the sexual side to our personalities. They are composed of all the scenes and sensations from our childhood, as well as early sexual experiences, that were somehow invested with erotic feeling. As children, certain sights, sensations, and smells became sexualized and act as an unconscious backdrop for arousal. For example, suppose when you were a child you saw your mother with her arms raised as she hung out the laundry. In a moment of exuberant love for you, she picked you up and hugged you close to her, your little legs wrapped around her side. This felt good to you, you may even have had an erection. This experience may have been stored, and thereafter, though you have no idea why, you find the image of a woman with her arms raised erotic. Perhaps when your partner puts her hair in curlers, or hangs a picture, or paints the ceiling you are swept away by a feeling of arousal.

All of our sexual, sensual experiences make up our libido and are available as material for sexual fantasy. The fantasy—the unconscious part of our sexuality—is crucial for arousal and orgasm. It is as necessary as the physical touching and movements in producing orgasm. In fact, some of you may be able to have an orgasm as the result of a powerful sexual fantasy without any direct physical contact. Some of our fantasies are so fleeting that they are hard to catch. Others are fully enacted scenes with characters and specific sexual acts. These fantasies may plunge us for several minutes into an erotic story. Most of us have at least one sexual fantasy a day. Some occur while we are attending to the business of the day, such as working or driving, and some occur while we are thinking about sex. When we make love, it is both the physical events and psychic images that increase our arousal and lead to climax.

Like dreams, our fantasies come out of our unconscious, expressing parts of our sexuality. We are comfortable with some and explore them in our sexual life. Others we would never explore, and a few are so fantastic that they are impossible to actualize. Fantasies may involve taking on different roles. Like Rachel, you may imagine yourself a helpless kidnap victim or maiden in distress. Maybe you fantasize group sex or a homosexual episode.

Many of you replay especially memorable sexual scenes from your past. Or perhaps you imagine yourself meeting a sexy woman on an airplane and letting her seduce you. Maybe you imagine the careful seduction of a virgin or the wanton aggressiveness of a vamp. These sorts of fantasies usually involve someone other than your spouse, and they require you to behave in ways that do not always fit with your typical personality. For example, you may usually be a considerate lover, but in your fantasies you may be a domineering partner who thinks only of your own pleasure; or maybe you are usually absolutely open about your sexual intentions, and in your fantasies you are a skillful tease. You can use your fantasies to arouse yourself or to increase arousal during sex. In any case, your sexual fantasies are fertile with ideas and emotions, a rich reservoir from which you and your partner may draw.

AS PRIVATE FOREPLAY. You may find yourself becoming aroused by your fantasy. Specific scenes or sights may be guaranteed to turn you on. Maybe picturing naked breasts or imagining a leaping dancer in tights sparks your sexual interest. Perhaps you find yourself lost in reverie at the sight of a good-looking man's body jogging or a billboard of a sexy woman. As you fantasize a sexual episode with this attractive stranger, you are aware of a dampening of your panties or a growing erection. Sometimes this seems to come out of nowhere, unstructured and unbidden by your conscious will.

You may well know what images are arousing to you and return to them again and again whenever you want to be sexually stimulated. Maybe you and your spouse have scheduled a time to make love, and you want to be sexually free and excited. Give yourself some time to imagine one of your favorite sexual scenes, replay one of your prior lovemaking sessions, or imagine events you would like to try later that night. You can use your most potent images to increase your arousal and intensify your lovemaking that night.

DURING SEX: Most of you fantasize during sex. More than 75 percent of men are aware of having fantasies during intercourse. Some of you may have fantasies you do not remember, or of which you are unaware, although they serve to kindle your responsiveness. You may find yourself focusing on a specific part of your lover's body. Perhaps you picture your lover's buttocks arching and relaxing or imagine your penis sliding in and out of your lover's vagina. You may replay prior episodes or picture an imaginary person also performing sexual acts with you and your spouse. You may imagine that your spouse is a different person. All of these fantasies are an expression of your own libido.

You may be able to use your fantasies during sex so that your arousal keeps pace with your lover's. You know which of your images are most intense. As your lover grows more and more excited, you can picture your own most powerful images. This will increase your arousal so that your passions climb simultaneously. Likewise, you can use less erotic images to temper your excitement. You men can use fantasies to time ejaculation (although some of you may be so focused on your partner's responsiveness that the signs and thoughts of her arousal are enough to help you time your ejaculation). You may also decide which fantasies are useful for you. Suppose you are aware that your wife is not quite as excited as you and you wish to delay ejaculation. Perhaps you picture her fully clothed or imagine that you are just beginning to make love to her by kissing her breast. After a few minutes, you become aware that her excitement has surpassed yours. Then you could imagine a more potent image—such as her hotness squeezing your penis or her panting for more of you—so that your arousal coincides with hers. You women can use your own most potent images as you become aware of your husband's swelling ardor. You may replay intensely arousing fantasies when you sense his impending ejaculation.

Using sexual fantasies during lovemaking enhances couple sexuality. Often erotic images and fantasies are totally unconscious, unbidden, and unremembered. But this does not need to be so. It is in the conscious summoning of your sexual fantasies that owning your sexuality is most fully acknowledged. Your love and caring for your partner, your desire to please and be pleased, are served by the joyful manipulation of your own powerful fantasies.

USING FANTASIES AS IDEAS. You and your spouse can portray different roles together. By play-acting, you can become all possible women, you can become all possible men. Additionally, you are exploring a new part of yourself, learning more about different aspects of your sexuality. Robert had no idea that Rachel wished to be carried off and ravished. She seemed like a perfect example of the modern liberated woman—independent, efficient, open about her needs and desires. But one day she decided to see if she could get him to play a sexual fantasy with her. It started out simply enough. They had been jogging together; both of them were in good shape and proud of the physicality that existed between them. She challenged, "I bet you can't catch me," shouting over her shoulder as she sprinted on ahead of him. He caught her and she struggled out of his grasp, panting with exertion. They were almost home and she bounded up the stairs to their house. She jumped out at him, teasing him with tickling. The hunt was on, and the two of them ran around the house like two kids chasing each other, tickling, wrestling, hiding and seeking.

The closeness and excitement were becoming increasingly arousing—Robert's erection and the hardening of Rachel's nipples were obvious to them both. The tempo of the chase changed; they clung to each other longer, teased each other with seemingly innocent touches. Robert couldn't help it if his thigh ground between her legs when he caught her. Rachel couldn't help it if she panted in his ear from exertion while wrestling away from him. The signs were clear, and Robert finally picked Rachel up and carried her upstairs—kicking open their bedroom door and throwing her down on the bed. While holding her down, he gently caressed her, tickled her skin with his tongue, blew on her wet flesh till goose bumps of eagerness and excitement stood out on her skin. Rachel realized that they had played a new game, had discovered a new way to initiate sex, a new way to heighten eagerness and passion. She had been captured and carried off.

Rachel had used her sexual fantasy to initiate a different kind of sexual contact with her spouse. You, too, can do this. If you find yourself especially excited by a certain fantasy that you imagine time and time again, see if you can actualize it. Talking about your sexual fantasies with your lover brings you closer, since you are sharing a private part of yourself and learning more about your partner; then together you can decide if you want to play out your fantasy.

Talking About Your Sexual Fantasies

BEDTIME STORIES. In order to feel comfortable talking about your sexual fantasies, you first must feel comfortable talking about sex. Suggestions made earlier in the book may help make talking about sex easy. When you feel comfortable discussing sexual wishes and preferences, you can move on to share sexual fantasies. This requires the ability to put aside your censoring self and free-associate. You learn to put into words the images that race before your mind and increase your imagination. Think how exciting practicing this skill can be! You become a Scheherazade, weaving a spell of intrigue and enticement. The walls of your bedroom can become a movie theater, with a cast of characters encapsulating you in their spell. A Dungeons and Dragons game of seduction and arousal, you tailor-make a tale guaranteed to arouse you. Telling a good sexual story and weaving a mood of eroticism is a skill and a talent. See if you have it.

Like any skill, this one improves with practice, though some of you may find it easier to do than others. At first, you may feel inhibited and speechless. Maybe you could start with a scene from a book or a movie that you found erotic. Let your imagination soar, filling in those details of time, place, season, position, and players that seem most arousing to you. Think of your last sexual fantasy and describe it to your mate (it will change as you tell it, different aspects coming to the fore). You and your lover could take turns telling fantasies or make up a fantasy together in which one person starts off and the other adds a part. For example:

HE: A man was sitting on a park bench. It was spring. A woman walked by with a poodle and sat down next to him.

SHE: The woman began to feed the pigeons. Soon there was a cloud of pigeons surrounding them, blanketing them from the world.

HE: The woman began to take off her clothes, slowly unbuttoning each button, concentrating as she slid the fabric of her clothes off her limbs. She wanted the man to take off his pants. She had cast a spell on the pigeons, who agreed to hide them from the world.

SHE: The man moved closer and began to move his hands up and down her body, sending chills and goose bumps all over her flesh. His touch was soft. It was almost as if he weren't there. He kissed her passionately, their bodies pressing hard against each other, trying to melt into one.

HE: She begged him to enter her, to take her. He rammed into her. Later she said he was a most marvelous lover.

SHE: After they were dressed, she told him she often walked her poodle in that park. If he waited every day, perhaps she'd see him again.

SHARING YOUR OWN SEXUAL FANTASIES. You may tell your mate your own sexual fantasies. At first this may make you feel vulnerable, exposed. Your fantasies may seem forbidden or "dirty," if they're about activities that make you feel ashamed or embarrassed. Many of you may have fantasies about acts you would never wish to actualize. For example, you may fantasize about being raped or committing a sadistic act or a sexual activity with an animal. Feeling that your lover would be disgusted or frightened makes it difficult to share these secret thoughts. But fantasies are not realities; thinking is not doing. Your fantasies are a different aspect of your sexual self, and you may wish to share these parts of you, too. Making yourself vulnerable and sharing this concealed self enhance closeness. It exposes part of your sexual unconscious, allowing both to share a common set of erotic symbols. Sharing sexual fantasies is arousing by itself and can be part of your foreplay.

Jane had a sexual fantasy that embarrassed her. She would imagine that several men were surrounding her, watching her. One of these men was the "leader" and was instructing the other men on how to arouse her. He circled her nipples, moving slowly down to her belly with a feather. As he aroused her, he described to the other men what he was doing and pointed out the effect that each stimulation had. Gently teasing the hair curled over her clitoris, he noted that she was arching her back and spreading her legs, eager for him to explore the folds of her vulva. The other men all stood around watching her performance, impressed with her sexuality and her orgasmic potential. How could Jane share this fantasy with John? Wouldn't the mere existence of all those men make him feel that he wasn't enough for her? Perhaps he would feel that she was some exhibitionistic person, or someone who might be interested in group sex, which, in reality, intimidated her. Jane was afraid her husband would misread her or would think less of her.

John always assumed that Jane had sexual fantasies; he supposed that almost everybody had sexual fantasies of varying degrees of complexity. He sensed that some of those fantasies could be easily shared, such as mentally undressing a woman and making love to her. Some of his fantasies were replays of his own sexual experiences; he would savor the sexual event, embellishing each motion and each position. Some fantasies were difficult to share. They seemed to come from parts of him that were not like the rest of his personality. He was a gentle and kind man, proud of the true equality with which he treated women. Occasionally he would find himself imagining a rape scene, during which he would drag a woman and force himself on her. At the climax she would give in passionately, wanting more and more of him. His arousal and sense of pride were clouded by his feelings of shame and self-disappointment. He was afraid that if he told Jane she would react with moral outrage, and he needed her acceptance.

One day John decided to try to talk with Jane about his fantasies and to find out more about hers. Slowly they both began with fantasies that seemed more "acceptable." He told her of imagining stripping and then making love to strange women, and she told him of fantasizing about making love in a train. Their acceptance and curiosity about this new exploration encouraged increased openness. Jane was able to share parts of her fantasy; John, aroused by it, decided he could play the part of the "leader." Then John felt comfortable in sharing his rape fantasy, and the vague sense of guilt he had about the rape scene was finally banished. Each of them felt closer to and more accepted by the other.

Like John and Jane, you, too, can learn how to share your fantasies with your mate by going through ever more daring and risky stages. You must feel comfortable talking about sex. The accomplishment of each phase enlarges your comfort, your capabilities, and your skills. Give yourself plenty of time to integrate your new skills. Stop when you feel like it, going only so far as your own comfort allows. Then, if you wish, move on to the next step. First tell your lover what you like through praise, then move on to making direct requests. Request poker, letters, or erotic money can make this step easier and add an element of fun and games.

When making direct requests becomes almost second nature, you can try talking during sex, if you wish. You can add a running commentary or describe your feelings and sensations. At the point when these skills are incorporated into your sexual repertoire, the two of you may decide to talk about your sexual fantasies, finally weaving them into "bedtime" stories. Sharing these parts of yourself will enhance the closeness between you, and perhaps you can even polish your skills until your story is sexually erotic. Your fantasies are information the two of you can use together. You will learn about your lover and share your own sexuality when you tell each other your fantasies. Additionally, if you wish, you can use the scenarios from your sexual fantasies in your lovemaking, thus turning your fantasies into reality.

Playing Out Your Fantasies

Nancy used to like to pick up men. Sometimes she would go to a bar, or a chamber music concert, or an art show opening. When she was single, a one-night stand was terrific. She loved the challenge of using body language to send signals across the room. She would look the man up and down, waiting for him to notice and then look away, dreamy-eyed. Then she would glance at him from the corner of her eyes, slowly run her index finger around the lip of her glass, and lean over to pick up her purse. Usually it worked and the man she had picked out responded. It felt terrific, as if she were in control.

Then she met Nathan; Nathan changed all that. Nathan, to whom she felt totally committed, totally in love. She knew now that her one-night stands had been a way to feel more powerful in a situation in which the woman was usually passive, waiting. Instead, she had done the choosing, the initiating. She was beyond all that now, sure and confident in her marriage with Nathan. Yet she found herself replaying those old days when she'd been the huntress, aiming herself at her prey. It had been exciting and very different from her current relationship with Nathan. But she was much too committed to jeopardize her marriage by picking up some stranger and screwing him. She might get herpes or VD, and she would certainly feel guilty at the betrayal of her commitment to Nathan and their marriage. She knew that would be acting out, endangering all she had built.

Yet she thought about it more and more; and finally she decided to play a seduction game with Nathan. They had been out to the theater and stopped in a nearby bar for a drink before going home to the kids. The play had been a comedy and Nancy felt buoyant, adventurous. She went to the ladies' room, then ordered a drink to be sent to Nathan's table from an "unknown admirer." She slinked up to the table and said in her huskiest voice, "Are you alone? Would you like some company?" Nathan was confused and joked, "You must have gotten amnesia on the way to the john." Undaunted, Nancy continued, carrying on a conversation with him as though he were a stranger. She crossed her legs high, so that the slit in the side of her dress opened as she suggested that he buy her a glass of Bordeaux. Nathan caught on and soon they were both in the swing of it, holding back their chuckles as they made up preposterous stories about their lives to seduce the other. At last they could contain themselves no more and laughed as they drove home. It felt a little as if she had picked him up. Somehow, it made her feel like the swinging single again, the huntress who had hit her mark. She had captured the feeling of adventure she had dreamed about without hurting her marriage.

There is a difference between acting out unconscious fantasies and playing out conscious fantasies and games. The example above elucidates this principle. If Nancy had gone to the bar and picked up a man, she would have been acting out her feelings, but by pretending to pick up her own husband, she was playing out her fantasies. In acting out your fantasies, you are a couple driven by feelings and patterns beyond your awareness. You are not feeling your feelings, but acting them out without any sense of what or why you are behaving as you are. When you play out a fantasy together, you are holding on to it, feeling the feelings it engenders, accepting that part of yourself. In playing out your conscious fantasies, you are a couple exploring different roles, different aspects of yourself and your lover. You are playing together. You are not mindlessly repeating a pattern or behaving to meet unconscious needs.

The distinction is paramount. It is the difference between plunging yourself into a crisis to get rescued and pretending to need help so your spouse gets to rescue you. Thus, it can be the difference between sinking the family into debt and an evening's seductive entertainment. It can be the difference between doing a slow, sensual strip for your wife and being a flasher, exhibiting your genitals to shock and dismay. Playing out your curiosity about bondage by gently tying your lover to your bed is different from acting out your need to dominate by tying up and torturing someone. Pretending to be a submissive "geisha" for one night is vastly different from acting out the need to give of yourself by becoming a virtual slave to a system that ignores the needs and feelings of women.

Yet the idea of playing out your fantasies may feel awkward. Perhaps it may even scare you. Maybe you feel that playing out one fantasy will open up a Pandora's box, lead you, perhaps, to acting out fantasies that now seem forbiddden to you or perverted. You may thus refuse to play out any fantasy, to avoid finding out about parts of you that you feel are unacceptable. All fantasies are acceptable; fantasies and thoughts are not the same as deeds. Once you recognize a fantasy, you can decide whether you wish to do it.

There are some clear rules you and your lover can use to help you feel comfortable playing out your sexual fantasies. Obviously, you both must be willing to do it. But no fantasy that causes psychic or physical pain should be played out. Fantasies are not sexual ends, but preliminaries, as are initiation and foreplay. Playing out fantasies gives a nongenital set of feelings free rein, thus enhancing the entrée to come. Fantasies add variety to your sexual relationship because they change the seduction routine or the foreplay. Most of your fantasies are seduction fantasies, a change in place or person or role.

Seduction Fantasies

Most of us have fantasies we would like to play out. Perhaps some involve a change of locale, such as making love in a hotel room, in a train, or in your office. Some involve a change in the role of seduction. They all tap into your fantasies, call upon the child in you to pretend and play out a creative drama. Below are some fantasy games you both can do to change your roles in initiation.

PICK-UP. Earlier in this chapter, you saw how Nancy changed her usual role with Nathan by "picking him up" in a bar. You and your mate can play many variations on this theme. You can agree to arrive separately at the same place—a restaurant, a disco, a cocktail lounge, even a PTA meeting—and pretend you don't know each other. Then, one of you makes a move to get to know the other. You can take on a different persona completely, perhaps pretending to be a movie star, an astronaut, or a Nobel Prize-winner. You can choose a different profession, marital status, or hobby and explore the new persona you have created. Each of you can play out and pretend to be someone you always wanted to be.

Of course you can also be just who you are. You can turn to your spouse and ask her what she does for a living or how he keeps his beautiful body. You would then have a conversation similar to one with any stranger and show enthusiasm for accomplishments and interests. You'll see a different side of your same old spouse this way. When you first got to know each other, you were different people. You impressed each other with different aspects of yourself. Now, you may take your mate's achievements, good qualities, and talents for granted, and this is a way to highlight and reappreciate them.

The first few times you play this game, you may feel awkward, laughing and giggling at your stiff attempts to be a famous ballet dancer or a Russian spy, feeling phony at pretending to be enthusiastic about your spouse's skiing, which seems sometimes to hamper smooth family life. But with practice it will become easier and you may find that you really enjoy the playfulness and the romance of it. You will be pretending your spouse is some other character or a new romance and yet be able to rely on the trust and security of your relationship.

GEISHA OR GIGOLO. Mae wanted to completely take care of Martin. She wanted to pamper him, spoil him, make him feel like a raja or a prince. She planned an entire evening catering to his needs. She ran a bubble bath, scented candles were lit around the bathroom. She had purchased a soft natural sponge. When Martin came home, she let him know this was his evening to be adored. She slowly undressed him and suggested he soak in the bath. Then she bathed him, kneeling outside the bath and scrubbing him, rinsing him with the soft sponge, gently caressing him. When he got out, she dried him, then massaged him with oil. A dinner of his favorite foods had been prepared, and she fed him, sharing a glass of wine with him. Occasionally she let him feed her. She let him know his wish was her command. Would he like her to read to him, or would he like her to make love to him? He was to lie back and relax, he was the focus of the evening. Mae had tried to translate everything she knew about the practice of the Oriental geisha into Western practice.

Geisha can also be gigolo, in which the male partner pampers, adores, and creates an evening for the sensual and sexual pleasure of the spouse. This is a special treat for your lover, a way to show love and perhaps to play out any fantasy you have about being a geisha or gigolo.

If you wish, this game can become whore and trick. Many of you have fantasies about being a prostitute, a high-class call girl who commands hundreds of dollars for her night's work or a male prostitute who pleasures women for money. Together you can play out this fantasy, having a session of lusty sex, in which one of you is in control but pretends to be out of control with passion.

PIRATE. Pirate is another version of sheik, in which you are carried off and captured. Earlier in this chapter you saw how Rachel seduced Robert into playing sheik by teasing him into a chase game. This is a game that really requires two complementary fantasies. One of you must wish to be carried off and captured, and the other must have the urge to do the capturing or kidnapping. You can use the skills you developed in the pick-up game to pretend you are a pirate or kidnap victim. You get into the persona and then pretend you are capturing your lover and holding him for ransom. The excitement of this game comes from the captured person having no control or responsibility for the sexual events and the sheik or pirate being strong and all powerful.

TEENAGER. Jason decided to take Janice to a drive-in movie. He hadn't been to one in well over a decade and it seemed like a novel thing to do. The picture was one of those horror movies he had loved as a boy—scary and exciting, producing a mixture of fear and adrenaline like a roller-coaster ride. He remembered nostalgically how his dates had always moved close to him during the scary parts, how in the second feature they'd spent most of the time necking, practicing their kissing. Janice got a big box of popcorn and a six-pack of beer, and they settled down to watch the movie. Just like when they were teenagers, by the time the second feature was on, they were more into each other than the screen story.

Jason rained kisses on Janice's face, creating a trail of tender touches down her forehead, the side of her face, her neck. He traced the curve of her ear with his tongue. Janice responded by kissing his eyebrow, the ridge of his nose . . . and his mouth. Tentatively, teasingly, they began to explore each other's mouths with their tongues. They kissed each other's necks, and ears, and hands. They left hickies everywhere. They were aroused and wanted to get home so they could finish by making love.

Maybe you, too, have forgotten the simple joy, the exquisite pleasure of kissing. You may have ignored this as a seduction, focusing on genital foreplay techniques. Perhaps you used kissing as a way of greeting or a brief first step in sexual initiation. Yet kissing is one of the most erotic of acts, something you can participate in equally, simultaneously. The mouth and tongue and cheeks are our first sensory organs; we learn about the world through our mouths. The tongue, lips, and palate are all focuses of sensation. Kissing all by itself can be satisfying lovemaking.

The fantasies you and your mate can play out are unlimited. You know what images, what scenes turn you on. They are your own daydreams, you own erotic respones to a scene from a book or movie. Perhaps you would like to stand under a flowering tree, hidden by the pink branches, and kiss your mate, your bodies pressing close. Maybe you'd like to revive the childhood game of "doctor." Perhaps you would like to play a game of hide and go seek, running and hiding, chasing and finding, kissing and grabbing, wrestling and hugging throughout your house. Maybe you'd like to play damsel in distress and have your husband rescue you from an imaginary dragon. Perhaps you'd like to be a virgin all over again and have your spouse pretend to teach you how to make love, how to kiss, caress, and move in the motions of intercourse. Maybe you've always had a secret thing for Santa and wondered what was really in his bag of treasures, so that you find it particularly erotic when your spouse dons a Santa suit for the kids at Christmas.

Playing out your seduction fantasies can enhance your sexual relationship. You are adding variety to the initiation of your sexual contact. Because the purpose of playing out a fantasy is to add variety, once it becomes a part of your routine it will have lost its power. No matter how exciting "pirate" is to you, if you and your mate find that you feel compelled to play "pirate" before each and every sexual occasion, then "pirate" becomes stale, old hat, and dull.

TRUSTS

In addition to playing out fantasies in the initiation and seduction part of your sexual relationship, you may also wish to play out fantasies in the sexual joining itself. Perhaps you have a fantasy of a new position for intercourse, or perhaps you fantasize making love orally to orgasm (or, like the couple in an earlier chapter, trying anal sex play). Playing out these fantasies entails owning your sexuality and feeling comfortable asking for what you want. Embarking on any new sexual adventure requires that you take a risk and trust your mate. This trust is especially relied on in trying out bondage or dominance games.

A LITTLE LIGHT BONDAGE. Zelda wanted to explore a different side of her sexual character, a side about which she felt strange. She had always had a fantasy in which she was totally controlled and dominated by a man. Sometimes when she and Zachary made love, she imagined that she was the character in *The Collection*, tied up and totally at Zach's mercy. She would be treasured and desired. Her sexuality would be so irresistible that she had driven a man to capture her. Somehow, in her magical fantasy, he would know exactly what she wanted. He would know all her most erotic spots, her secret favorite positions, her most delicious private fantasies. He would sense them, and then make her do them. She would not have to ask to have her nipples sucked, she would not have to ask for him to put his finger in her vagina. He would know. He would do. She would not be responsible, would not have to own her sexuality, simply allow it. In her fantasy, he would even order her to come, and she would.

Zelda knew and trusted Zach. He was a good man, he knew and understood her sexuality, accepted it, relished in it. She trusted him completely and totally. She knew he would never hurt her, could never get carried away and even for a moment forget who she was—his friend, his lover, his lifelong mate. A four-poster brass bed went on sale, and on the spur of the moment, she bought it. She put it up and got a new set of satiny sheets. Zach loved the new bed and heard her serious request beneath the tease when Zelda pointed out the virtues of their beautiful new bed by saying, "And those posts sticking up in the air are perfect for tying me up."

By dusk, Zachary had it all planned. He took over the sexual interlude completely. He bound her wrists with his ties and knotted the ends to the posts. Pretending to be an arch villain, he chuckled in mock glee, saying, "At last I have you in my power. Now I can do with you as I will. You are helpless and at my every whim. . . . Heh, heh." He began to caress her, softly tickling her body with a feather, touching her. She twisted away from him, trying to get away from his tickles. He slid his hands down her thighs and grasped her ankles, then tied them to the posts. Zelda was spread-eagle on the bed, unable to move, to respond, to resist. Zach then made love to her. The sexual contact was not out of the ordinary. He aroused her with kisses, excited her with touches, entered her gently, and moved his body. But she could not move. She could not touch him, she could not move her hips to his rhythms. She lay there able only to respond with her vaginal muscles. Her sexuality was in his hands. Somehow her inability to move, to be active, was extremely arousing, exciting. She couldn't do what she most wanted to do. Her orgasm was powerful.

Zach liked tying her up, too. He loved being in control, being the master. It fed his latent macho fantasies, and he enjoyed seeing her squirm with delight, then lie helpless while he gave her pleasure. Later, they reversed it. Zelda tied Zach up with silken cords and pleasured him. He lay helpless on the bed, and she caressed, sucked, licked, and teased him until his erection seemed ready to burst. Then she mounted him, moving as he lay inert and in her power while she pleasured him.

Bondage is one of the most prevalent fantasies, which is the reason why pornography about bondage is one of the most popular-selling subjects. There are many reasons why bondage fantasies are so erotic. Almost everyone has rape fantasies and bondage is one way of playing this out. Additionally, there are power and domination issues throughout our culture and in male-female sexual relationships. The woman's movement sprang up as a means to achieve a balance of power between men and women. Penis envy may now be explained as an expression by women of their jealousy and rage, not at a man for having a penis, but at a man for having the power that accompanies that organ.

All of our sexuality is present in childhood; our unconscious sexual language and erotic nature are being formed then. During our childhood, we are helpless and vulnerable, necessarily dominated by our parents. Perhaps the potency of bondage is contingent on the degree of that domination and is then reinforced by the culture in which we live. Both sexes have in their sexual psyche the twin aspect of domination—being dominated and being the dominator. But because of cultural reinforcement, men usually have fantasies in which they dominate, while women's fantasies involve being dominated.

There is some evidence, too, that compression of the wrists and ankles, thumbs and big toe, soles of our feet, and elbows increases sexual feeling. Perhaps this is related to the ancient Chinese pressure points for acupuncture. Also, recent research indicates that sexual feeling may be intensified after experiencing any other adrenaline-producing emotion. A study was done in which students watched a frightening horror movie and were then introduced to people of the opposite sex. The movie had increased their adrenaline, and they found the new people much more attractive and sexy than a control group did. So perhaps the adrenaline produced by the fantasy of bondage and by the pretend struggle enhances sexual arousal.

Many of you may wish to play out your fantasies in a little light bondage. For some of you there may be a secret thrill in being gently tied. This, too, takes two complementary roles. One of you is in power, pleasuring the other. One of you is helpless, allowing sexuality. You may wish to switch roles or take turns being bound. One of you may wish to be blindfolded, not even able to see what delicious sexual plan your partner is enacting. Your focus is only on your sensations. Perhaps one of you would like to be gagged, only able to moan your pleasure. You don't need to go out and buy a four-poster bed. You can tie your lover's wrists and ankles together, tie them to the bed legs, or use a post. Clearly, gentleness, consideration, and common sense are important. Never, never wrap or tie anything around your partner's neck. Don't leave a person who is tied up, and only tie your mate up for a short time. Make sure the material you use to bind the person is not too hard; laundry cord is fine. You can buy all sorts of exotic-looking equipment—leather hoods, straps, gags. Chains and handcuffs are too hard, difficult to lie on, and do not compress.

The trust that exists between you is called upon in bondage and is also fed. Being tied and gently made love to proves yet again the safety of your sexual relationship, the trust you have in your partner. You are truly handing over your body to your lover, and your lover treats it gently, with respect and awe, pleasing you, loving you. For you, the one with the power, you know the responsibility and trust your partner has in you. You have proof that your lover has absolute faith and confidence in your love and caring.

DOMINANCE AND SUBMISSION. Dominance and submission games create power structures similar to those of bondage, but do not require physical restraints. Again, there are two roles. The submitter is the ultimate extreme of the "geisha" and must do whatever the partner requests. The dominator gets to order the partner to do specific sexual things. What you are really playing is parent and child, and for some of you this may arouse special feelings of sexuality. There is a wide range of continuum of dominant and submissive behavior. You can request a behavior, and your partner, out of love or duty, may feel constrained to honor that request; you can also threaten or cajole your partner into submission. Most of you will play the game somewhere in the middle. You both decide in advance that one honors acceptable sexual requests, with a mutual understanding of what constitutes "acceptable." Domination that involves humiliation and discipline is not helpful to maintaining a close, mutually respecting relationship.

So the game is in the roles rather than in the behavior. And, as in the playing out of any fantasy, if you feel compelled to play a game of dominance and submission or bondage in order to enjoy yourself sexually, then your coupleness is endangered. The game then becomes the point of the sexual interlude, your partner's unique individuality is denied and lost in the scenario of the game. But occasionally playing out a game enhances understanding of your lover's individuality.

Fantasies and trusts add new horizons to your sexual relationship. They are doorways to understanding more about you and your mate's sexual unconscious, and they can be used to add variety to your sexual contact.

9

THE SEDUCTION OF PREGNANCY

Ann stared with awe at her body; she could hardly believe the changes it was going through. Her breasts were lush and now tipped with darker, protruding nipples. Her stomach had swelled and a dark stripe arrowed to her clitoris. She was ripe, she was a Venus screaming out her fertility and the promise of life and renewal. Her pregnant body was an obvious testament to the passionate union she had had with her husband. Her body was changing as it was supposed to, as had billions of other women's bodies in aeons before her. The life now within her was a culmination of the changes that had started in her childhood and pushed her to womanhood.

In her adolescence she had been too shy and insecure about her own sexuality to glory in the changes in her body. Now she was impressed by the universal stamp of pregnancy. She imagined somehow she was on display, her sexuality obvious to the world. She proudly wore her maternity clothes. Life was moving within her, twisting and caressing her from the inside. A miniature person was growing, a person complete with fingerprints and hair and—if it was a girl—ovaries developed to carry her genes and Aaron's to their grandchildren. The miracle of a life was about to be, the creation of a human being, and all because she and Aaron had made love.

Ann loved being pregnant; she glowed, she was euphoric, her energy seemed boundless. Her world was truly touched by a rosy glow, smooth, loving, and ideal. Their sexual relationship was better than ever; the pregnancy awakened Ann to new sexual possibilities and experiences. And Aaron was glorying in their new sexual adventures. He saw her swelling belly and enlarged breasts and knew his body had had an impact on hers. The growing proof of their sex was arousing to him, making him feel proud of his masculinity. The very delight with which she greeted her changing body was encouraging to him. He felt the life they made kicking under his hand, strong and sure. He adored her body and the miracle they were making together.

By the beginning of her second trimester, Ann was feeling more sensual, more aware of her own body than before. Maybe part of this was stimulated by the vaginal exercises she was practicing; they certainly seemed to have increased the ease and power of her orgasms. Maybe it was that her vagina seemed exquisitely sensitive, so that each subtle movement from Aaron was felt from deep within. She was multiply orgasmic for the first time; she felt as if she were a tinderbox ready to go off at the touch of Aaron's match.

As Ann's pregnancy advanced, the face-to-face intercourse that had brought such new joy had to stop. Her growing belly became a hard, uncomfortable ball preventing their bodies from pressing close together. Their increased passion would have to find another outlet and spur them on to discover new ways to express their lust. They had found such pleasure in the missionary position that they had left other positions largely unexplored. Rear entry intercourse, with Ann lying on her side and Aaron entering her from behind and caressing her breasts, back, and clitoris, became a new favorite. No matter how large their baby grew, in this position Ann's belly was safely out of the way. The clitoral stimulation was even more intense with Aaron's fingers than it had been with his body movements, and Ann loved the feeling of Aaron's penis spurting when he came inside her.

Feeling free sexually, they were eager to develop other aspects and possibilities. They honed up their oral-genital skills. Before, oral-genital contact had been largely relegated to foreplay; now they began to explore its possibilities as the main event. Ann loved it when Aaron lapped her, gently and tenderly, bringing her peace and rocking orgasms at the same time. And Ann, with new wisdom and excitement, devoted herself to sucking, licking, and appreciating his organ. Aaron vibrated to this, feeling powerful and well loved. Together they used their pregnancy to stimulate and enhance the very passion that had created it! They felt so close, each so understanding of the sexual psyche of the other. They continued intercourse throughout Ann's pregnancy. In fact, they made love on the day her labor started; the shooting of Aaron's sperm and Ann's orgasmic contractions encouraged the progression of her labor. Their love for each other had been expressed by a beautiful act and that joining had created a new human being. They were awestruck at the power and beauty of their love and felt existentially united, their baby proof of a glorious mating.

Ann and Aaron found pregnancy a truly sensual, sexual experience. Never before had they experienced such lust, such oneness. Never before had they understood the power of their love and passion for each other. They felt as if they were all human beings at all times, creating the species again and anew. They delved into each other's sexual psyches, learning new ways to please each other, using the impediments of the pregnancy to push them on to new inventions and new ways of expressing their passion.

Not all couples respond to pregnancy with increased passion. Pregnancy creates a new and special set of biological and psychological sexual variables that may alter your sexuality during this period. All of you are different and each of you handles this barrage of feelings in your own unique way. Use this time to learn about each other and about the experience of pregnancy.

Feeling Good About Your Pregnancy

Your reactions to pregnancy cannot be simply predicted. Your feelings about being a reproducer, a female animal, a mother—your sexuality in this broad sense—partly determines how you feel about your pregnancy. Additionally, the hormones of pregnancy affect your physical and emotional well-being. Finally, your attitude about your body and the monumental metamorphosis it undergoes affects how you feel during your pregnancy.

ACCEPTING YOURSELF AS A FEMALE. How you react to your pregnancy will be partially determined by your feelings regarding your sexuality in its reproductive role. Pregnancy, childbirth, and breast-feeding are the reasons our female bodies are made the way they are. Our bodies are uniquely designed to carry out these functions. Reproduction is the reason for the difference between the sexes. Our sexual impulses are powerful, controlling forces in our lives, so much so that we lust to propagate the species. This desire—almost a deep need—is especially keen when we embark on a new love affair. Many of you will find yourselves fantasizing about having a baby, thinking continually about infants, feeling impelled to procreate as a result of the powerful sexual feelings you share with a new lover. You yearn for a baby to become a visible, living proof of your love, of your joining.

Your comfort about your relationship with your mother and the traditional role of women also have an impact on your own pregnancy. Your own parting from your mother's body to become a separate woman, sexual and pregnant, repeats an age-old cycle. In being pregnant, you are accepting your mother in a new way; you are agreeing to journey down a path she has traveled. By accepting a traditional woman's role, you are letting your body define the course of your life, at least to some extent, for some time. You have no control over the changes your body makes, over when your baby is born, over how often or how long she cries at night. Somehow, you must juggle all other aspects of your life around this. Your career, your exciting conversations with your women friends, your physical activities, the when and how of your sexual relationship are all dictated first by the pregnancy and then by the baby. You have agreed to give some control of your life to another. This crucial fact dawns on you initially during pregnancy, and your reaction to this receptive, nurturing female role will impact on your feelings about your pregnancy.

Pregnancy, childbirth, and breast-feeding are inherently sexually unequal. It is the woman's show. You the man helped start the process but thereafter can merely stand by, applauding, encouraging, respecting, and being in awe. It is your wife's body that almost seems to explode as the baby grows within her, it is her body that contracts, rests, and contracts painfully yet again. It is her body that strains to push the baby out into the world. It is her breasts that fill with fluid to feed the baby. All these are, although common, truly amazing spectacles of nature. And in all of these you are left out. No matter how balanced you and your mate are in your roles as breadwinner, chore-doer, and sexual partner, you cannot equally share this huge task. You cannot carry the fetus for her, cannot labor to bring it forth. This only your wife can do. There is no more unequal aspect of your lives together.

As a woman you may glory in the receptive, nurturing role, accepting and encouraging the feelings of dependence and vulnerability that flood you during pregnancy. You may wish for nothing more than a nice cozy cave where you can make a safe nest for your infant and have your mate provide food and protection. Or you may feel threatened by the inequality, terrified by such archaic fantasies, afraid all the other parts of you are being swept away by your body's demands. You may fear that the equality you and your husband so carefully built will be forever jeopardized. You may worry that you are becoming merely a reproducing animal—a person forever defined by a child.

Clearly, your feelings about your new role will affect your sexual responsiveness with your husband. Your joy or anger, acceptance or rejection in subtle or not so subtle ways affect how you are sexually. You may become more passive or more active, withholding or receptive, depending on how you are processing all these issues.

DEALING WITH THE CULTURAL NORM OF THIN-

NESS—"I'M NOT FAT, I'M PREGNANT!" Our culture holds in very dear regard the ideal of a woman who is thin, almost bustless and hipless, with a tight, firm stomach. Pregnancy is the opposite of this ideal. During pregnancy, your breasts get larger, your nipples bigger and darker, and a dark line often extends beneath your breasts through your navel to your pubic area. Pads of fat line your shoulders, hips, and thighs (there to be used as a calorie source during breast-feeding in case of a dwindling food supply). There is often a swelling of ankles and hands, a puffiness around the face. Your body can no longer meet the criteria of beauty held up in our culture.

Moreover, there seems to be little idea of what a pregnant woman looks like. Perhaps until recently women in their last trimester had been carefully tucked away. When you are pregnant, people feel free to make remarks regarding your size. This is in direct contrast to the usual reticence in our culture regarding a woman's size. You may be surprised when at first your friends can hardly believe you are pregnant because you don't "show" enough. They may react as if you must be wrong about your due date. Then, as your pregnancy advances, you may be continually greeted with, "Are you going to have twins—I bet you're going to have twins," "Are you overdue?" and "Your baby is due any day now, isn't it?" This may be disconcerting to you. Your psyche can barely deal with your body's changes as it is, and comments by others only confuse and alarm you. When you are around other pregnant women, you are reassured to realize you are all pretty much the same size at the same stage. You may be amazed at how huge you are shortly before birth, however. take some pictures of yourself at your most pregnant, proof of how large you were shortly before you gave birth.

How do you deal with being so different from the cultural norms of feminine beauty and the comments from other people regarding your size? How do you maintain your view of yourself as sensual and sexual when you are so far removed from the ideal of thinness? Betty could not reconcile her pregnant body with her previous self-image. She stared with disgust at her body. She could hardly believe the destruction that this pregnancy had wrought. Her breasts were distended, and blue veins were visible beneath her skin. Her nipples were growing so, they looked as if they might swallow her whole breast. She could hardly bear to look lower. Her belly button was bulging and brown, turning inside out! And there, above her pubic hair, she could see the beginnings of stretch marks turning her smooth, tan belly into a spiderweb of angry red-and-purple wounds. Her chic, high cheekbones were lost in the puffiness of her face, and her body contours were hidden under pads of fat. Pregnancy was just not made for the modern woman, she thought, and it was certainly not for her, when she had always taken such pride in her athletic body, slim waist and hips, and pointed breasts with nipples almost the same color as her flesh. She had always maintained an almost model-thin frame, the envy of her friends.

To make matters worse, Betty was tired all the time. After three months of vomiting or feeling nauseated, there was this constant tiredness, which seemed to be assuaged only by eating. She was always constipated, and so short of breath that even climbing a flight of stairs left her panting for air. She tried to remind herself that she must stop to rest halfway. Betty's belly was so big now that movement was difficult. She struggled to get out of the sofa, hoping someone would offer a hand, and she needed to make a three-point turn to roll over in bed—almost like parking a car. The list of complaints seemed endless. All Betty thought about was her body—fat, tired, constipated, hungry, and almost immobile. Sex seemed out of the question. This pregnancy had taken over her body. She could hardly wait for her baby to be born, so she could again be thin and agile. She felt like a hippopotamus or an elephant, not a beautiful woman. A friend remarked, "Betty, you're more feminine, more female, now than you were before. Before you were thin, now you are an earth mother!" Betty was startled by this idea—it was a new way to view her condition, a new image to consider. Perhaps it was a way out of her current dismay.

Betty's disgust with her body, plus the exhaustion and illness caused by the pregnancy, made her disinterested in sex. As with Betty, your feelings regarding the cultural norms determine how you view your body. This period in your life will be harder for you if you subscribe to the *Vogue* model image of beauty. Try on a new image for a while—the image of "earth mother." Large and fertile, swollen with life, the pregnant you represents an ancient ideal. You are like a goddess who was worshipped for the evidence of her fertility, magically guaranteeing an abundance of food, prosperity, security. Surround yourself with images of the earth mother, all giving and nurturing, strong and loving, caring and able to receive the needs of others.

Use your own imagination to bring forward this new image, pushing the slender model standard to the background. Imagine yourself as this important symbol, bearer of life, the essence of womanhood and sexuality. Feeling that power within you can help you enjoy the new largeness and ripeness of your body. Adopting the mind-set that your pregnant body is a new, beautiful, lush you can help you to glory in your changing body. You can further define the changes as beautiful by studying the ideals of beauty from other times, such as the huge-breasted, protruding stomachs of bygone Venus, the bulges of a Rubens Sabine woman, even the large-breasted, rounded hips of a Marilyn Monroe. Think of yourself as powerful, strong, the wellspring of growing life shouting to the world with your bodily changes. Remind yourself you are woman incarnate creating a new human. Close your eyes and relax; recall all those pictures of lush womanhood. Hush those old voices about slenderness with new ones about being an earth mother. Use these images to fight against the barrage of propaganda that thinness is the essence of femininity. Obviously being pregnant is more the essence of womanhood than being skinny.

Enjoy your pregnant body while it lasts; after all, pregnancy is only a short nine months. Pamper yourself and heighten your sensuality at the same time. Massage your growing belly and breasts with a special body cream; enjoy a luxurious bath as you rub yourself with fragrant oils; take a leisurely nap in the afternoon or a walk on a multicolored fall day. Buy yourself perfume, flowers, beautiful nightgowns. Appreciate the smell, color, and feel of your new body and the world around you.

THE IMPACT OF YOUR HORMONES. The hormones of pregnancy orchestrate the changes in your body. The implanted embryo sends out programmed messages that regulate the timing and flow of hormones. Physically, these hormones impact on women in similar ways. Psychically, the hormones may be experienced differently. Each of you experiences a unique pregnancy each time. Some of you will feel tired the first trimester; some will vomit; some will feel terrrific, buoyant and full of life. Obviously, if you go through your pregnancy bone-tired, hungry, nauseated, constipated, and bothered by heartburn, you are going to feel different about the changes your body is going through and the new role you are about to assume. Likewise, if your pregnancy is easy and you feel fabulous, you may feel being pregnant is the preferred state and have an easier time dealing with your body's changes and the new role.

Terry felt she was being propelled by her emotions. She never knew what to expect from one month to the next. At first she was so cranky it was almost as if she were rejecting Ted. Then she felt terribly vulnerable. If he was late for dinner, she was sure he was flirting with some other woman. If he brought her flowers, she was moved by his love and thankful for his caring, and her eyes brimmed with tears. She could cry at the mention of an ill animal or a happy ending. She felt emotionally exposed. Sexually she wanted mostly to be rocked. Terry felt like a small child and Ted's arms were like pillars protecting her. She wanted only for them both to stay home making a quilt for their baby.

Now she felt entirely different. Powerful. Able to do it all. Her pregnancy was an advertisement for her sexuality. She fantasized doing a strip tease onstage, an audience of men staring up at her, aroused by her beauty, awestruck by her sexuality, her vigorous movements. When she and Ted made love, she wanted to take charge of their activities and exhibit a new sexual passion. She loved these strong feelings but also loved the softness of her vulnerability.

You, too, may find new feelings surging through you. As your baby's kicks are first felt, you may find yourself always watching for more. You may be involved in your body and the sensations within, the changes without. As never before, you may be so absorbed in yourself, your baby, that you become less and less aware of what's going on around you, unable to concentrate on anything but the momentous process happening inside you. This new narcissistic involvement with yourself is a falling in love with the pregnant you—with you and your baby. Like Terry, you may vacillate between feeling vulnerable and extremely powerful. You may brush aside all physical problems, certain you can accomplish anything one day, merely to feel unable to move the next. You may feel like Wonder Woman, and then feel like you want to crawl into a secure cave while your mate brings in food for you to cook. One day you may view sex as a source of comfort and security, wanting your mate to shelter you in his arms, soothe you with his rocking body. Another night you may want his applause as you take the stage to display your sexual prowess and exhibit your new self for admiration.

Thus, your pregnancy influences your sexuality. The hormones surging through you, your acceptance of the female, life-giving role, your view of your new body—all impact on your sexual relationship with your spouse at this time.

Some of you will feel intensely sexual. Your engorged vagina may make you more sexually sensitive. Perhaps you are doing Kegel exercises and learning how to control your vaginal muscles. These exercises may increase orgasmic capabilities, thus heightening your sexuality. You could be feeling exquisitely female and powerful, free and sure of yourself in a new sensual way. Some of you may feel disinterested in sex. No matter how thrilled you are about the pregnancy, how secure you are sexually, or how fabulous your sexual relationship with your husband has been, your libido during pregnancy may diminish. Dealing with the physical changes and emotional swings of pregnancy may command all your emotional attention.

As it is for women, so it is for men. Your husband, too, will have feelings about your body, about his role as father, and about the traditional role you both will assume. As it is for you, so, too, do all these factors impact on his sexual feelings during your pregnancy. This new sexual reality presents a challenge for the couple.

Being Sexual During Pregnancy

Not all couples are as lucky as Ann and Aaron, not all of you will be aroused by your pregnancy. But all of you can learn and explore new aspects of your sexuality, engendered by the biological and psychological alterations of pregnancy. Each of you can learn to enjoy sexuality in your own way, each way is a valuable and important part of your sexual life as you grow and learn from the experience of pregnancy.

Jean's pregnancy presented a great challenge to the sexual relationship with her husband, Jack. Sex had always been easy for them, a given in their relationship. They loved the missionary position and no matter what foreplay preceded, they always came "home" to face-to-face intercourse, where they enjoyed simultaneous orgasms. It seemed so simple and perfect—each of them pleasuring themselves and each other at the same time. Jean's pregnancy changed all that. Jean was glad she was pregnant. She had always wanted to be a mother, and she and Jack had felt this was the perfect time in their lives. Jean was interested and curious about the changes in her body and she supposed, as pregnancies go, hers was relatively easy. She had been slightly nauseated the first trimester and now, at the beginning of her seventh month, she was feeling tired. But she couldn't understand what all the fuss was about—it wasn't as great or as terrible as it seemed to be for many of the women she knew.

Her interest in sex had diminished and she didn't care if she ever had sex again. She liked being close with Jack and cuddling, although her growing belly was making even that difficult. Jean remembered their passion, their easy and comfortable unions, and figured that would come again. But now sex just seemed cumbersome, difficult, second best when compared to the simple beauty of their prepregnant intercourse.

Jack was turned off by Jean's body. He wasn't disgusted, just less interested. She seemed vulnerable to him, and he worried that somehow he'd hurt her. He didn't like the looks of her large belly.

Her skin was stretched so tight it left red marks, like wounds, across her abdomen. He never did like large breasts and now Jean's breasts seemed to already belong to the baby. And her navel looked sore and had turned inside out. Jack could hardly remember lying directly on top of her, enjoying the smoothness of her body and the suction that developed when their bodies moved together. Worst of all, he could not stop thinking of the baby when he was with her. Jack could feel the baby moving, and when he and Jean finished making love, the baby seemed to protest by kicking vigorously. He imagined his penis hitting the baby's head, Jean's cervix and vagina a thin membrane separating him and his child. Maybe he would hurt the fragile baby. When Jack felt sexual toward his wife, he remembered the baby and it was as if they were never alone anymore, almost as if he were making love to two people at once. Sometimes it felt as if the baby were spying on them.

It was very hard for Jack to talk about his feelings. Jean had noticed his lack of sexual interest and was concerned for their future sexual relationship. Was he permanently turned off by her or was he just being considerate? she worried. Finally, she expressed her worries to him and he talked about his feelings. Jean could understand that Jack would be afraid of hurting her or the baby and could also respect his feeling that their baby was already a conscious human being. Jack reassured Jean that her prepregnant body was extremely attractive to him. He knew that his fear of hurting her or the baby was not based in reality, but his images and feelings would not go away. Jack was relieved that Jean had reacted to her pregnancy with a decrease in libido. In talking over their feelings, they realized that the pregnancy had brought forth new feelings for both of them, feelings confined to the pregnancy, thus having no impact on their future sexual relationship.

Jean and Jack, though, needed to decide what they were going to do about sex during her pregnancy. They both remembered their previous sexual relationship with nostalgia—the easy, lusty couplings—and knew that would return. They decided to express the sexuality they still felt through oral-genital sex, which Jack felt would not hurt Jean or their baby. They took turns pleasing each other; first Jack kissed Jean's vulva, then Jean sucked Jack's penis.

Sometimes, Jack would caress Jean to orgasm, and then he would enter her from behind for his pleasure. They enjoyed pleasing each other but did not like "taking turns" sexually; it was not their sexual style.

As the pregnancy advanced, more and more of their feelings of closeness and love were expressed through cuddling. Cuddling had never been a large part of their relationship and now it suddenly became important to both of them. All their feelings of tenderness, affection, and love were shown in this way. They would cuddle on the couch while watching TV, cuddle for hours in the morning. They felt so safe and secure in each other's arms, they hardly wanted to leave the bed. At night, they would lie caressing each other, staring into each other's eyes, anticipating the birth of their baby, talking about their dreams, their plans for the future. They tantalized each other, detailing all the sexual avenues they would explore when Jean's belly was no longer a hindrance.

They loved practicing the Lamaze breathing techniques, discovering more and more about each other's bodies. Jack and Jean learned how to sense tension, first by touch and then by a mere glance. They practiced breathing and comfort techniques together. The energy they had previously spent on sex was channeled into teaching each other to relax, giving each other massages, and trying to learn more about each other's bodies. Toward the end of Jean's pregnancy, they practiced perianal massage. Jack stretched the area between Jean's vagina and rectum, massaging with vitamin E oil, hoping to minimize the need for an episiotomy. Soon they felt close to each other in a new way; knowing each other's bodies more completely had augmented their understanding, respect, and companionship. Together they had used Jean's pregnancy as a discovery period, providing them with feelings and experiences they could draw on for years to come.

SHARING YOUR FEELINGS. Pregnancy presents you with a new set of sexual circumstances both psychic and physical; there are changes in the woman's body and in the man's and woman's feelings. You will find that pregnancy stimulates changes in your sexual relationship. Some of you will feel intensely sexual, or perhaps you will feel that sex during pregnancy is a bummer. Throughout your pregnancy your sexual appetite may change; you may feel exhausted the first trimester, lusty the second, and disinterested the last three months.

The first step in maintaining a close sexual and sensual relationship during pregnancy is talking about your feelings. Knowing that this can be a difficult, frighteningly exciting time and that other couples, too, have qualms and anxieties may make the expression of your feelings easier. You may have had romantic fantasies about the course of the pregnancy. Perhaps you imagined that you and your mate would glory in the changes, redefining the sexual bond as one that created life. You imagined that your passion would continue unabated, strong and powerful. But this is not how it always is.

You and your mate may react to the pregnancy in ways that surprise you. However you react, let the feelings wash over you, lead you, teach you. There are no right or wrong ways to feel during pregnancy. Your feelings are there for the two of you to explore together. Your emotions may be new for both of you, and the two of you together can learn from them. Your mate needs to know your feelings. Even though you may feel vulnerable, even though it may feel hard to share your feelings, this is the only way for the closeness between the two of you to continue to grow and deepen. And remember: Your feelings, and those of your mate, are temporary. Pregnancy ends. The emotions that may be buffeting you about right now are tied to a temporary physical state, caused by and related to the pregnancy, not you.

Some of your lover's feelings may be hard to bear. Maybe you hate your large, cumbersome body. You may be turned off by the maternal image your wife now represents. Perhaps you are extremely turned on and your mate seems disinterested, making you feel rejected and unloved. Maybe you want to forgo sex until after the baby arrives. No matter how you feel, the first step is talking about your feelings. The second step is listening as a friend, hearing what your mate is trying to say, while both of you remember that together you are exploring a different, but temporary, aspect of your sexuality. You are sharing your feelings to keep your sexuality alive, exercising the compassion you feel for one another, and guaranteeing that during this time, too, your sexuality and sensuality will be shared.

THE NEW PHYSICAL POSSIBILITIES. You and your mate understand each other's feelings and are eager to continue your physical closeness. There is a new physical reality to deal with. Being able to talk about sex will now begin to pay off.

INTERCOURSE. There seem to be different opinions regarding sex during pregnancy, so you should check with your physician to get a medical opinion pertinent to your particular pregnancy. Traditionally, physicians advise against intercourse from six weeks before to six weeks after birth, a total of three months of abstinence. Now, many physicians feel intercourse throughout pregnancy is fine; some suggest that intercourse in the early stages of labor may hasten birth either through the orgasmic contractions or the spurting of the semen against the cervix. Intercourse can only promote a labor about to begin; it cannot start a labor prematurely. After your bag of waters has broken, however, refrain from intercourse to decrease chance of infection. There is evidence to suggest that having intercourse when you would have been menstruating may cause spotting, possibly even a miscarriage, particularly during the first trimester.

After you get the go-ahead from your doctor, the two of you can have fun experimenting with various positions. Some will be possible at one stage of pregnancy and then, a few months later, uncomfortable. Different body types and size of genitalia may make a position terrific for one couple and impossible for another. This is a time for a "different strokes for different folks" attitude as the two of you experiment. Intercourse can be tricky when there is a thirty-centimeter wedge between you and the object of your desires! Together you figure out ways to continue to join. You both may try positions that are funny or find yourself in hilarious situations. Your imagination may outrun your flexibility or stamina. You may feel like gymnasts trying to meet around a ball. Although your contortions may provoke more laughter than arousal, your sense of humor, imagination, and love will make sex fun, sometimes funny, and always loving.

As your body gets larger, it will begin to feel uncomfortable to have your lover lie directly on top of your enlarged uterus. You can't hurt the baby, as it is floating in its amniotic fluid, but the pressure can be unpleasant. Thus, your growing belly may literally create a wedge between you, making missionary-position intercourse impossible. For a while, woman on top of man will work, with the woman sitting astride. Since penetration is deep, this position may also become difficult as you reach the end of your term. You can lie down on the edge of a bed or table, and your husband can stand or kneel to enter you. The advantage of this position is that it allows you to face each other. The disadvantage is finding a table or bed that is the same height as your husband's genitals.

Another position you may want to try is with the woman lying on her back at a forty-five-degree angle to the man, who is lying on his side. One leg is over his body, the other is between his legs. His top leg, then, can fit between her legs, and he is able to enter her. He must be careful not to rest the weight of his leg on her growing abdomen. Again the couple is able to look into each other's eyes, touch each other, and there is no weight on the uterus. Throughout pregnancy a rear-entry position is possible. With both of you lying down, the man can caress your back, breasts, stomach, and clitoris. Your growing belly is safely out of the way and presents no hindrance.

During pregnancy, too, changes in lubrication and the blood-engorged vagina may make penetration difficult; the woman may feel dry no matter how excited she is. A water-soluble lubricating gel, such as K-Y jelly will help ease penetration.

NONCOITAL SEX. Pregnancy can be used as a time to explore and delve into noncoital ways of expressing sexuality. Mutual masturbation and oral-genital sex are perfect outlets during this time. Do not blow or force air into your wife's vagina; this may create serious, sometimes fatal, complications. The physical limitations of pregnancy do not impede improving techniques for fellatio and cunnilingus. You can kiss, lap, tickle your lover's genitals with your tongue, learning how to tease and prolong the pleasure. You sense in another way your partner's readiness for climax. You can also learn from watching your lover masturbate, seeing how your lover turns himself on or how she moves to please herself. You understand what places, what movements, what tempos are most exciting at the various levels of arousal. Then you each can try out your new knowledge, pleasing each other and peaking your own passion with your prowess. Perhaps pregnancy is just the excuse you both need to learn more about these techniques and to use them not only for foreplay, but to complete the sexual act. This may be a time of "taking turns" sexually, where one of you makes love to the other and then you switch. Perhaps you kiss your lover to orgasm, and then your lover caresses you until you, too, come. You will both have used the physical limitations of pregnancy to enlarge your sexual knowledge and abilities together.

AFFECTION. Affection and cuddling are vehicles for your feelings of closeness and need for skin contact. Many of you will have positions in which you cuddle. Perhaps you snuggle against your mate with your leg and arm over his body, your head nestled in his shoulder. Perhaps you pull her toward you and like spoons facing in the same direction encompass her body with your leg and arm. You may fall asleep while cuddling and sleep throughout the night in each other's arms. You may wake up to cuddling, feeling that you need that close, warm contact before struggling to get out into the cool air and face the pressures of the day. You may cuddle on the sofa while watching TV, your arm around your lover, her head on your shoulder.

Affection is always with you. No matter how huge your stomach, no matter how tired or pressured you feel, showing affection with cuddling helps you give love and feel loved. Such skin contact seems to be a human need, so much so that pets exist to catch the excess affection and caressing we need to give. You can use affection to express the sensuality and love you feel toward each other. You may not wish to have sexual congress, to have an orgasm, but simply to be close and warm, loving and safe together. Sex does not always have to be expressed with orgasm. Your appreciation of your mate's body can be shown through touching, snuggling, cuddling, being close, and feeling each other.

Many of you will wish to go through childbirth together and will take prepared childbirth classes. Practicing relaxation techniques heightens awareness of different aspects of your lover's body. You learn how to effect relaxation, to recognize tension and pain. The breathing exercise also teaches you about your lover's body and the tempos of breath itself. Perianal massage—in which you insert your fingers into your wife's vagina, stretching it toward her rectum—may prevent tearing during childbirth. Your easy access to such a physically intimate act can thus be used to aid your wife during childbirth.

Together you can use pregnancy to enhance your sexuality. Allowing yourself to feel the new emotions pregnancy arouses and sharing them with your lover augments closeness and unifies sexual symbols. Your new biological realities may encourage experimentation in coital positions, in noncoital expressions of sex, and in uses of affection. Helping each other to prepare for the intensely physical task of childbirth also increases your understanding of the comfort with each other's bodies.

Childbirth

Giving birth to a baby is a peak experience. For many of us, it is the hardest thing we have done emotionally, physically, and intellectually. Our lover's support, caring, and love during labor eases our pain. As a man, your appreciation and respect for women and the start of life is renewed. As a couple, it is the culmination of your sexuality; your sexuality has created a new human being. It is a godlike feeling making a person, a feeling that the couple can share and experience together.

If you have decided to help your wife through her labor, your aid will be immeasurable. Women who have a coach during labor and delivery have shorter labors and less need of medication. You may feel scared some of the time. Your wife may know instinctively that everything is going according to plan, but you have no such instinct. Instead, you may be impressed by the pain, worried about the length of the labor, and unsure about whether the contractions are strong enough to ensure dilation. Long-buried fantasies may well up inside you. You may decide that the pain looks, sounds, and seems so terrible that you will never again put her through such an ordeal. Some of you may worry that you're too squeamish to be helpful to your wife, that you'd only pass out. You may be unable to separate the vagina bulging with your baby with the vagina that you love to penetrate. These feelings may inhibit your future sexual relationship. Your feelings need to be respected, you should not be pressured into going into the labor and delivery room if the prospect scares you. Follow your instincts in this; you know yourself best and know what you can handle and what might prove to be difficult in the long run.

Paradoxically, although childbirth is sexual experience—maybe the essence of sexuality, since it is the reason for our strong sexual feelings—it seems nonsexual in the way we usually think of sex. You, the laboring woman, do not think of pleasure or modesty, but only of the monumental task ahead, only of delivering your baby and ending your pain. Your vagina is no longer an organ for penetration and orgasm; it is a birth canal. The birth of your baby takes precedence, overshadowing all else and defining all. You tap into your primal emotions as you give yourself over to the extraordinary power of your body dictating what is happening to you.

Yet, in spite of the pain, some of you feel aroused during birth. The stretching of your vaginal walls, feeling the baby crown, then the head emerge, next the shoulders, and finally the slide of the baby's body have been perceived as arousing. After all, the uterine contractions and concomitant pressure on the vaginal walls are similar to intercourse and orgasm. Many of you will feel this as a burning or a tearing sensation. In some ways, childbirth may feel to you like another loss of virginity. Your vagina is penetrated yet again and redefined—a loss of virginity from the inside out. Again, you gain understanding and knowledge about another aspect of life.

The experience of childbirth may have an impact on your sexuality. This impact may be positive or negative. On the negative side, the pain, the blood, and the vast changes of the woman's sexual organs may be distasteful to you. As a man, you may find your partner's organs and pain so overwhelming that sex feels strange. You may hesitate to take the chance that she could get pregnant again. You may fear that your penis will be swallowed up by her body.

You may feel your wife has become only a "mother" and find it difficult to feel sexual toward her. If seeing your lover give birth will make you feel like this, then don't watch. Pace the waiting room instead. As a woman, you may never want to experience childbirth again and be terrified lest you become pregnant.

On the positive side, many couples feel the experience of sharing childbirth has improved their sexuality. There is a closeness created in sharing such a primal experience, which increases the bonds of love, understanding, and trust in each other. There may also be a feeling of increased sexual freedom, that the last barriers of modesty and sexual reluctance are forever banished. This may create a willingness to try new sexual adventures. As one woman stated, "He's seen it all already, I guess I'll try anything now." Some women find that there is a quiet and complete acceptance of themselves as sexual beings, an understanding that is total and mixed with a new sense of pride and self-love in being a woman.

Together as a couple you can use the experience of pregnancy to learn new things about each other sexually.

1. Use images of yourself as an earth mother to get in touch with your sexual beauty during pregnancy.
2. Accept your feelings and share them with your mate. Your ability to talk and communicate about sex will be tested and enlarged during your pregnancy.
3. Experiment with sexual positions that increase comfort as your pregnancy advances.
4. Enjoy noncoital and affectionate ways of being physical with each other. Don't force air into your spouse's vagina during pregnancy. Oral-genital contact and cuddling maintain sexual and sensual togetherness.

When you hear your baby cry, all your exhaustion and the memory of your pain will vanish. You both will feel a rush of emotions as you fall in love with your baby and each other all over again. Your love and sexual joining has produced the start of a new generation. Together as a couple you will help that new young life to become a citizen in the world of the future.

10

PASSIONATE PARENTS

Holding her new baby seemed a miracle to her. Sally was transfixed by the person she and Steve had made. For hours, they stared at Sara, their baby, melting inside from the wonder of it all. Her small circled toes, her delicate eyelids, her rosebud lips, her perfect whorled fingerprints. They could see parts of themselves transferred to her new body. There were Steve's lips and Sally's hands in miniature and given to her as gifts. Sara stared back at them with big dark eyes, stabbing into their souls, claiming them for life. Her baby felt so good, so right. It was as if Sally had been a puzzle missing a piece and this little baby finished her.

Sara smelled good, looked good, felt good. She seemed designed to be held, cuddled, adored. Her small stomach curved perfectly over Sally's breasts. Sara's head snuggled, filling in the hollow between Sally's neck and shoulder. The crook of Sally's arm seemed designed to support Sara's little head beneath her nipple or as a ledge for Sara's buttocks so they could rock together. Sara's skin was wondrously soft, even her little baby breath had a sweet smell. Seeing small Sara tucked in Steve's large arm, seeing him talk to their intensely staring infant, made Sally turn on to him in a new way. He was a more gentle, tender father than she had imagined, and she felt closer to Steve than ever. No one had told her what a sensual experience taking care of a baby could be. It seemed the most completely sensual experience of her life; she would want to go on holding, smelling, cuddling, caring for her baby forever. She was in postpartum ecstasy.

Early one Sunday morning, Sally and Steve were making love. Sally had climbed astraddle of him and was lost in the moment, aware only of her motions and Steve's rhythmical rubbing and squeezing of her buttocks. Sara, now four years old, had awakened and wandered into her parents' bedroom, standing inside the door, bewildered and rubbing her eyes. Suddenly Sara understood her parents' game and with a broad smile stated, "Mommy, I want to play ride the horsey, too!"

These two vignettes illustrate the impact of children on sexuality. Holding a baby, taking care of children, can be a sensual experience, keeping you in touch with basic emotions as you help a budding sexuality to unfold. You gain a new understanding of your lover after seeing your mate as a parent. Then again, there is no doubt that parenthood hampers couple sexuality, as when Sally and Steve were interrupted during sex. As a friend of mine quipped, "Children interfere with sex so much, it's a miracle anyone ever has two!" Issues of time, privacy, and spontaneity arise when you bring home your baby. These are the inevitable trade-offs for the full life and understanding you gain as a parent. In this chapter we'll find ways to maximize the sensuality of parenthood and minimize the trade-offs.

Sensuality of Parenthood

FEELING SENSUAL. Sally was responding to the sensuality of her baby as women have done for aeons. Babies must have been made to appeal to our senses, so that we would agree to take care of them. Those large, beautiful eyes staring so intently at us bonds us to them; that soft skin covered with down is a delight to touch; the way their bodies are formed to fit so perfectly on our shoulders, in the crooks of our arms, and over our breasts make us ache to hold them. And each baby has a delicate, sweet smell—no body odor or bad breath yet. Their gurgles and coos are little musical tunes, and their cries are so irritating we instantly rush to care for them.

Your breasts fill with milk, becoming painfully engorged; baby's nursing relieves this pain. Your baby is in bliss sucking and sleeping, sucking and staring at your breast until his peace produces a deep sleep. Breast-feeding is a pleasurable experience, as your baby's sucking is soothing and peaceful for both you and your child, simultaneously nourishing your baby and producing pleasurable uterine contractions in you.

As men, your hearts warm at the tenderness of your baby, a fragile life there for you to protect. Your baby's smile and cooing may enchant you, the excited grin, babble, and waving of her arms when you walk into the room let you know how crucial you are. Already the love forms a strong bond between you. You and your baby fit so well together, need each other so, feel so good to each other as an evolutionary guarantee for the survival of the species. The sensual appeal of an infant changes as you watch the sexuality of your child unfold.

CHILDREN ARE SEXUAL. The sexuality evident in your infant, and the sensual feelings that the infant may stir up in you, may come as a surprise. Your baby is a sexual being at birth. Your infant son will have erections; you may see this when diapering him or when he is nursing. You may see your baby daughter rubbing herself, squeezing her thighs, or moving her body rhythmically against your body, then a few minutes later become quiet. You may have just witnessed your daughter's first orgasm or orgiastic equivalent. Your baby responds with deep satisfaction to good feelings in his or her body. Such obviously pleasurable examples of infant sexuality may be disturbing to you or, without realizing it, you may respond with sensual feelings of your own.

Steve had such an experience one day while he was diapering his baby, Sara. He had fed Sara her bottle and while she was nursing, Sara had a bowel movement. Steve saw her little face get red, could feel her body tense and push the bowel out as she cried with the strain. Immediately she became fussy, not wanting the irritating bowel on her skin. As he was changing her, he noticed that the watery movement had gotten in the folds of her vulva. Gently he spread her labia and cleaned the genital folds with a Q-Tip and moistened cotton ball. Steve was concentrating on doing a good job of getting her clean. Sara made a gurgling sound and he looked at her face to find her smiling and wiggling, obviously enjoying Daddy's ministrations. She liked it when he touched her labia and the delicate tiny folds of her vulva. Steve was taken aback. At first he felt shocked that his daughter was already capable of such an obvious sexual response. He felt maybe he'd better stop and let his wife finish diapering her. But then he realized that Sara was a little baby showing him she felt good, responding in a normal way for a baby to a good feeling. She was reacting to a good feeling between her legs, just as she reacted to a good feeling in her stomach when she was full. Her smile and cooing were her primitive, nonverbal ways to tell them, "You make me happy!"

Later that night he told Sally what had happened while he was changing Sara's diaper. Sally said she had noticed that Sara loved having her diaper changed, having her skin free to the air, and being washed, particularly around the lips of her vagina. Even when she was first born and Sally had to clean the mucous discharge from her vagina, Sara would become quiet and seem peaceful. As Sally and Steve talked, it made so much sense to them. Of course Sara's genitals would already create good feelings! She didn't suddenly grow a clitoris and nerve endings in her vulva, she came equipped with them, just as she had come equipped with hands for when she would be able to pick up things and feet for when she could walk. Steve said he felt strange but also good. It was good to know that little Sara felt sexual pleasure, that she was complete in that way, too. She was a normal responsive human being. He felt a warm pride that she was so perfect, so capable. Sally said, "Yes, just think, before we know it, she'll know what to do with all those good feelings, have a lover of her own. I just hope she has as great a sex life as I do." And Sally nestled in Steve's arms at the wonder of her tiny baby growing into an adult woman.

THE CHILD AS TEACHER. Like Sara, your baby will have

sexual feelings and will respond to your care with sexual delight. The care you give your infant will enhance your feelings of sensuality. Babies take such delight in simple things—even feeling corduroy or taking a bath can be a sensual thrill to a baby. If you let her, your baby will teach you all over again the pleasure in skin-to-skin contact, in the sights and sounds of the world around you, and in the parts of your body. You will respond to your baby's sensuality and sexuality with pride in your own proficient nurturing.

As your baby concentrates on exploring his own body and reminds you of the good feelings your body can have, your toddler, in his lust to explore the world, keeps you in touch with your basic emotions. Your toddler has neither the time nor the skill to hide his feelings. All his emotions, his reactions, are there for you to see. Seeing his unbridled emotions may remind you of your own primal feelings. Your own childhood emotions have been locked within you, tempered by the requirements of civilization. When you see your child jump with glee at the sound and feeling of the fall leaves crackling, scream with terror at the clap of thunder, sob heartbroken and frantic when his blanket is misplaced, you recall your own pure joy, terror, and sadness. Likewise, your children experience the good feelings in their bodies, and all the new world is met with fresh senses: the slippery-smooth feeling of their bodies sliding in the bubble bath, the sensual smell of clean pajamas and sheets, the safety and comfort of being rocked in their father's arms. Caring for a small child whose pleasure, arousal, and comfort are evident strikes a corresponding cord in your memory, keeping you in touch with your own unadulterated, primal emotions.

Jean learned a lot from her son, John. She and Jack had a baby boy who was a laughing, happy companion. He taught her adult self about the child buried within her. When he rocked and sucked his thumb when he was sad, he was the image of her as a child. With a start Jean recognized that in her, as an adult, those behaviors had metamorphosed into retreating into her bedroom and rhythmically winding her hair with her fingers when she felt sad and misunderstood.

Moreover, in spite of her intimate knowledge of Jack, Jean had never really understood how a male body worked until she became a mother. In her day-to-day caring of John, she was comfortable with his body. She knew how to anticipate his motions and became almost as familiar with his body as with her own. Because of this, Jean realized, she was more comfortable with Jack's body. She had translated her knowledge of her son's body to her husband's and had a new awareness of Jack's body, how his penis would sway when he turned, how his testicles would hang if he kneeled and reached. The easy familiarity she felt in handling her son's body was transferred to her manner with her husband's and communicated itself in the very way she touched him, caressed him, and handled him.

As your child grows, you see your baby becoming a sexual adult. You see your daughter's breasts bud, legs and torso lengthen, hips round. You know, you remember your own feelings about your newly sprouted pubic hair. You see your son's neck, arms, and shoulders thicken, the down change to hair on his upper lip; hear his voice deepen. You remember the thrill, the fantasy, the excitement, the embarrassment, the joy, and the turmoil of adolescence. Then your children grow into fully sexual adults, with their own sexual experiences and feelings. Seeing your children's sexuality unfold and helping them to be loving, confident sexual people keep you in touch with your past, your own emotions, the life events of humanity.

RESPONDING TO YOUR LOVER'S PARENTING. You and your lover parent together. Together you see your children develop, grow, struggle, surmount. You see unknown strengths in each other, you support each other's weaknesses, fill in for each other's faults. This experience enhances feeling, respect, and love for your partner. Seeing your lover parent may be arousing to you. Perhaps you see your baby sucking on your wife's breasts, and the rightness, the simple beauty of that vision, warms you yet again to her; you want to hold her, kiss her, stroke her, enter her. Perhaps you see your husband's large hand gently wiping a tear from your toddler's eye, bandaging his cut and bleeding knee. His tenderness and caring arouse you and you want to hug him, feel his body press the length of yours.

It makes sense that the loving parenting of others is arousing to you. If you yearn to have children, seeing someone care for a child may arouse your need to have a child. For example, Jeff always felt aroused when he saw a woman with a child. Simply seeing a mother with two babies was erotic to him, and loving attention on her part to the child was even more so. Janice likewise was attracted to men who enjoyed children; she felt secure and safe with a man who would take time to talk, play, and be tender to children. Jeff and Janice realized their arousal was predicated on their own desires to parent; they knew that becoming a parent was so important to them that people who were not interested in parenting would have been impossible as mates.

We gain a lot when we become parents. Taking care of children is a sensual experience. Infants appeal to all our senses, and our children's expressions of pure emotion keep us in touch with our own emotions. Watching and helping our children's sexuality unfold reminds us of our own pregenital yearnings and adolescent excitement. Through sharing the experience of parenting with your lover, you learn more about his strengths and weaknesses, discover how to work together as a team. Watching your lover parent, the tenderness, the giving of love, and the caring can be an arousing experience. At each stage, your child helps keep you both fresh and alive. The sensuality of the baby, the primal emotions of the preschooler, the joy, discovery, and mastery of the elementary-age child, the power and excitement of the teenager in the first flush of adulthood—all are played out before you.

You and your child form a bond, and this bond is a precursor to the pair bond your child will form with a mate. In many ways, falling in love recapitulates the strong parent-child bond of the first three years of life. Through parenting, your awareness of life is rekindled; each stage is experienced through your child's fresh eyes and your own wisdom.

Getting Around the Trade-Offs

STAYING MAN AND WOMAN. The joy children bring into your life is not without its costs. It is a myth that children bring a couple together. They can be emotionally and financially draining. In fact, couples with children are unhappier than couples without children during the early childhood period. Couples who are not parents have happier relationships during the first seven years of marriage. Research also indicates that for most couples the happiest period in their lives is when child-rearing is completed. These facts raise questions with crucial answers for couples who are parents. What are the elements of child-rearing that create such strain in a relationship? What goes on in the relationships of nonparental couples to make them so happy? What can couples with children do to have the best of both worlds—parenthood and some of the happiness of nonparental couples? And how does a sexual relationship play a part in this?

In addition to enjoying each other as mother and father and working as a team in rearing your children, it is crucial to focus on the other ways you relate: as a man and woman, as lovers, as friends. Spend time alone together, maintaining your privacy, inject spontaneity into your sexual relationship; and relate as man and woman in front of your children. The sexual strains are evident if you allow your relationship as man and woman to erode, permit the demands and pressures of your day to destroy sexual spontaneity. It is all too easy to put your sexual relationship on a back burner and allow all the day-to-day requirements of child-rearing to take precedence. Your relationship provides a secure, loving home for your children, and sex is an important part of that relationship.

As the years go by, you and your lover see each other more and more in the role of "Mom" and "Dad." Together you share the important task of parent; this role takes an enormous amount of your shared time and attention. It is so important and so demanding, it can consume all others. Slowly, without realizing it, you may begin to relate to each other less and less as man and woman, less and less as individual people, and more and more as Mom and Dad, perhaps even calling each other by these terms. You are mother and father together, but you are mother and father only because you are man and woman together, two individual people who care about each other.

Both of you lead exceptionally busy lives during this time.

Whether you have decided on a traditional family, in which the woman does not work outside the home, or whether you are both involved in careers, you will be spending much of your time apart, and much of your time together will be spent with your children.

SPONTANEITY. If you have young children, the spontaneity of your life together is compromised. You and your lover can no longer hop off to a movie on the spur of the moment. You must call a baby-sitter, find one who is available the night you wish to go, arrange transportation to and from your home, and leave a schedule of your plans for that evening. All of these arrangements may necessitate as much as a week's, often several days', advance planning. Likewise, a picnic on a lovely spring day may feel like a week-long trip when you lug along diapers, playpens, car carriers, toys, and the like.

As spontaneity is compromised in other areas, so it is diminished in sex. No longer can you allow your passion to overcome you and make love on the living room floor in the middle of the afternoon. Your children may choose that time to bring a new friend to the house. It is difficult to respond to the tender passion of early morning sex when your baby is crying for his breakfast. And babies seem to have an uncanny knack of knowing when you are about to make love or have a romantic dinner for two and choose that time to begin to cry. No longer can you make love when and where you wish; there are time and place constraints that exist when you bring home your baby and persist until your children are sufficiently grown to leave home. This is an inevitable trade-off of parenthood. You diminish the negative effects of this by scheduling time to be alone together.

BEING ALONE TOGETHER. The lesson to be learned from nonparental couples is to spend time alone together. Cherish your relationship as if it were all you have. Don't always talk about the children, set aside time just to talk about what is going on in each other's lives outside your home. Use the suggestions in the beginning of the book: take trips, go out alone together. Perhaps you are so busy you must set the alarm clock to get up in the middle of the night to talk, to make love. You can go on vacation. You can go into your bedroom and "take a nap" while your children are busy.

You can schedule sex. The time the two of you spend alone together is made more precious by its rarity—stolen moments of intensity devoted to each other.

GOING ON PARENTHOOD VACATIONS. One way to recapture spontaneity is to take short vacations away from the children. Couples whose children are products of prior marriages and visit noncustodial parents are more fortunate in this respect. They have one or two weekends a month all to themselves, a built-in vacation from parenting. But everybody needs a vacation from parenting. The two of you can go off together leaving the children at home in the care of a baby-sitter, or you can send the children away and glory in your freedom to be with each other, making love without regard to the pressures of parenthood.

Just having your children away creates whole new location and time possibilities for the two of you. They can be off to camp, away for a week, the weekend, or even a night. You can send the children to a friend's house or their grandmother's house. Maybe you have a close friend with whom you can exchange baby-sitting, so each of you can have the opportunity to be alone for a weekend. Once it is just the two of you, you can glory in a few days of freedom—freedom to make love in the living room, freedom to make love in front of the fireplace or with your bedroom door open. You can stay in bed all day if you wish, savoring making love before and after breakfast. Alone, you can take a walk or have the luxury of browsing in a shopping center. It is a time for you to be lovers again, to devote time to keeping up your sexual relationship and to explore each other in new ways.

It may feel frivolous or selfish to you to send your children away just so you and your spouse can be alone. You may feel you can make love anytime, why make complicated arrangements for child care just so you can stay alone in your own home? Yet the two of you need the time, especially when your children are small, to stay in touch with each other—emotionally as well as sexually. Your time alone together will feel like stolen moments, much like a summer romance that you know will shortly end. You and your lover can capture a month of passion in a weekend. Even an overnight quickie may revitalize an entire sexual relationship.

MADONNA/WHORE DUALISM. Some of you may be plagued by madonna/whore dualism and find you are unable to enjoy sex after parenthood. You may feel that women who are mothers should not be sexual, but should be like a madonna, disinterested in sex. As a woman, you may find that your sexual urges ebb away. It may seem inconsistent for you to be a mother during the day and a passionate bed partner at night. Sex no longer interests you, and you find excuses to avoid making love. The psychological aspects of your lack of sexual desire may be shrouded with the difficulties of getting your sexual relationship back on the track in the postpartum period or by the exhaustion you feel at the end of the day from taking care of small children. The source of this problem is your relationship with your own mother. You may be unable to accept your mother as a sexual person and believe that good women, good mothers, aren't sexual. Society colludes with you in this, and you may have struggled throughout your life with being both a "good girl" and a passionate woman.

For men, the problem usually has a more sudden onset. During your wife's pregnancy, or following the birth of your baby, your sexual feelings for your wife may vanish. Unconsciously, your wife's swelling body may terrify you. Your baby nursing at her breast may make your penis shrink. Without realizing it, in becoming a mother your wife has become your mother. Sex with her is incestuous, sex with your wife is taboo. You may thrust yourself into work or find yourself obsessed by sexual feelings for other women. You may fantasize about or embark on an affair. The source of your problem also lies in your relationship with your mother, your need to see her as asexual.

Mandy and Michael's relationship faltered when she became pregnant. Mandy had always had difficulty owning her sexuality—she felt that it should be shielded, hidden, like her vulva when she remembered to keep her legs crossed. She had learned the lessons her mother had taught her very well. She was affectionate but had trouble being passionate and was proud of her reputation in high school as a cold fish. Mandy certainly couldn't imagine her parents being sexual; why, she hardly saw them touch each other! Her mother was always so cool and composed that she couldn't imagine her losing herself to passionate abandon. Then she met Michael and felt sexual stirrings that she expressed with passion. She was no longer a cold fish but enjoyed the rude bodily contact and her loss of control during orgasm. She loved all these new feelings but found herself pushing Michael for marriage, partly to relieve her guilt at no longer being a virgin.

After marriage, Mandy thought she had combined being passionate and being "good"; she was "a lady in the living room and a whore in the bedroom." She found that motherhood reawakened her dilemma. When Mark, their son, was born all her attention was focused on him. Michael wanted to resume their sexual relations, but Mandy complained that it still hurt, and then that she was too tired. They still had sex, but her mind was elsewhere. She was always listening for Mark's cry. Her passion was gone. Mandy lavished love on Mark, keeping him with her, constantly cooing at him and kissing him. Michael started to feel that he had been pushed out of bed by his own baby. Mandy felt that Michael was being selfish and immature. In desperation, Mandy and Michael started therapy. It wasn't until they had been in therapy for a while that they were able to see that Mandy had incorporated the pattern of the asexual mother—that only "whores" enjoyed sex, while mothers were not sexual. Through looking at her own mother and untangling the messages that she had been given, as well as recognizing the double standard our culture sustains, Mandy was again able to be sexual.

After childbirth, your breasts will decrease, your stomach will tighten up, the stitches will heal. Your sexual interest and capacities will be as they were before pregnancy. However, if you or your lover believe that mothers should not be sexual, than your sexual feelings and the intensity with which they are expressed will not return to your prepregnant state. If you find that your interest in sex is low, even after your baby is weaned, it's time to search yourself to discover if you have incorporated the image of the nonsexual mother. If your wife no longer appeals to you after she gives birth, you may have swallowed our society's double standard. Children may create hurdles in your sexual relationship, but continual and lengthy lack of interest is not one of them.

If you find that you are disinterested in sex following the birth of your baby, here are some ideas that may help you:

1. Define the problem: Search yourself to see if you have incorporated society's attitudes that mothers are not sexual. You may be entirely unaware that this is the reason. You may feel tired or bored with the idea of sex. But these feelings are symptoms; the problem is your feeling about sexuality and motherhood. Is your wife beginning to feel like your mother? Are you beginning to feel like your own mother? Sometimes simply defining the problem helps. When you realize your lack of interest is the result of feelings stirred up by the birth of your baby, you may find your sexual interest beginning to return.
2. Deal with the realities: Your wife is *not* your mother. Making love with her is not incest! You are not your mother and mothers are erotic women capable and able to respond sexually. Beginning to incorporate these attitudes may help. In addition there is much literature available on this issue.
3. Go into therapy: If you've tried the first two steps and are still feeling disinterested, and if your sexual relationship is causing you pain, go into therapy. Such lack of interest is your psyche's response to motherhood and your own mother, and therapy can be helpful to you.

PRIVACY. You are no longer alone. Children require more planning for when and where you make love. Someone else can see you or hear you. Sally and Steve were distressed when Sara walked in on them while they were having intercourse. The spell had been broken, the passion and sexual feeling vanished. At first they were embarrassed. They felt caught. They felt almost as if they had been doing something wrong. Then they felt concerned that seeing them make love would hurt Sara. They had read that children who had witnessed the "primal scene"—i.e., parental sex—were emotionally scarred. The children interpreted the sexual act as an attack. Sally and Steve felt they were bad parents—certainly other parents somehow managed to prevent being walked in on like this! After they had time to think about it, and even to realize how funny it was, they knew from Sara's comment—"I want to play ride the horsey, too!"—that she hadn't interpreted her parents' sexual act as an attack but had seen it as what it was—good fun.

The next weekend Sally and Steve were at a party with some close friends and began talking about children "catching" parents making love. Several couples mentioned that their children had witnessed or heard parental sexual acts. One reported that a wise twelve-year-old could tell when his parents were making love because Mommy always laughed so much and then a few minutes later Daddy went, "Aaaaaahhhhh! . . ." Another walked in while his daddy was sucking on his mommy's breast and asked, "Is that something we keep in the family—a secret not to be shared with anyone else?" The parents were embarrassedly laughing, distressed at being caught and unsure of how to handle their children seeing or hearing parental sex. No matter how cute and funny their children's comments and misconceptions, they all would have preferred their privacy.

It did not seem too unusual for a child to see his parents having sex—and that reassured Sally and Steve. If it were such an ordinary event, maybe it couldn't be as traumatic as they had read. They had tried to treat it as matter-of-factly as they could, discontinuing intercourse and telling Sara, "No. Mommy and Daddy were doing something private and only they could play." They had decided not to give any further explanation unless Sara asked directly. She had seemed satisfied and wanted Sally to make her French toast for breakfast.

Sally and Steve were unsure of how traumatic it could be for her to witness them making love, but they did not want Sara to walk in on them again. They both knew it diminished their own enjoyment and, since it was definitely not something Sara could participate in, could leave her feeling left out. They decided to increase the soundproofing of their bedroom and to make sure their bedroom door was locked when they made love.

As passionate parents, you need to maintain spontaneity while ensuring privacy. How much privacy is a question of great debate. There are theories that suggest any witnessing of parental sex may be traumatic. There are other theories suggesting that the entire family should sleep together. The cuddling and comfort the children receive will decrease the feelings of loneliness and isolation so bothersome in this society. Moreover, children witnessing parental sex have been the norm in many other cultures throughout human history. So there are opinions and theories at both ends of the continuum. The safest approach seems to be somewhere in the middle. Your child's whole psychic world will not crumble if he sees you making love, particularly if you take it as casually as possible, answering questions honestly and simply. Additionally, your child may need the comfort of sleeping with you when he feels particularly frightened by sleeping alone or is troubled by nightmares.

However, having your child continually in your bed does interfere with your privacy. It leaves you little time to be two adults alone together, to feel free to try new sexual adventures, to moan and groan if you please without worrying about disturbing your children. Also, it is hard to know how your child will feel seeing you make love. Perhaps she will feel shocked, perhaps he will feel aroused. But frequently seeing you do something together and not being able to participate is likely to heighten feelings of jealousy, of being left out. Your child may feel excluded and lonely. In this case, it seems better to be safe than sorry.

YOUR BEDROOM. Your bedroom can be arranged in such a way as to maximize privacy. Lock your bedroom door. If you do not have a lock on your doorknob, use a hook and eye. This is so obvious and yet is so often neglected. Either way, you are guaranteed that your children will not disturb you in the middle of a passionate interlude. Teach your children to knock on a locked door. Then, if they should need you when you are making love, they'll knock or call and you can quickly go to them. You may wish to unlock the door when you are finished making love so that you can be easily available should your children need you.

You can also add soundproofing to your room. You can add a sound-deadening sheet or extra insulation between a wall you and a child share, or you can put cork or carpet on that wall. Make sure your bed and your child's bed are not against the same wall. If you do not find it distracting, you can play a radio or stereo. White noise, such as a fan, air conditioner, or sleep machine may also help prevent your children from overhearing you. Many of you may buy intercoms so that you can hear when your baby cries. Check to make sure you've pushed the proper buttons or your toddler will hear every sound made in your bedroom. Assuring privacy increases your sense of freedom, thus adding to the sensual aura of your room.

KISSING IN THE KITCHEN: OWNING YOUR SEXUALITY IN FRONT OF YOUR KIDS. You need to ensure privacy, not only for your child, but also so that you and your mate feel as free as possible sexually. Now comes the tricky part. While maximizing sexual privacy, you must be careful not to throw the baby out with the bath water by communicating to your children that you are nonsexual. You are sexual adults. You do have sex together and enjoy it. Your children want not to believe it. Your child would prefer to believe that his mommy and daddy never "did it." When scientific knowledge confronts him, your child acknowledges that "maybe Mommy and Daddy did it once so that they could have me and one more time for my little sister. They must have wanted us awfully bad!"

Our society conspires with your children to deny your sexuality. Madonna/whore dualism rears its ugly head and you and your children together deny that it is okay to be sexual and a mother. It is important that your children see you as sexual people. First, because you are sexual and to collude with their denial is a lie to them. Second, because one day your child will be an adult, a parent. It will be easier for your daughter to continue being sexual and a mother, for your son to continue to be sexual with a woman who is also a mother, if you have presented the model of sexual parents.

How then do you walk the line between letting your child know that you are sexual and yet maintaining your privacy? It is good for you to allow your child to see you touching and kissing. Sally could always remember how secure she felt when she saw her parents kissing in the kitchen. Her tall, dark father had swooped up her mother in his arms. It was not one of those ordinary "I'm home from work" kisses, but a movie star–type kiss, long and deep. There Sally's parents were, their arms entwined, their bodies pressed close, their eyes closed. Sally could still remember her thoughts: "My, they still do it. And they still love each other, want each other." She felt a warm, safe feeling spread through her.

As it was for Sally, so it is for many of your children. They sense the love you and your spouse share when they see you touching. They know there is still a romantic spark between you, a bond that holds fast. Particularly in this day when divorce is so common, the knowledge that there is something beyond them that their parents share may be reassuring. Go ahead and touch each other. Kiss each other passionately. Hold hands. It is okay for your children to know you make love. If you feel like making love in the afternoon, go into your room and lock the door. When you are on vacation, get your children a separate room, explaining that Mother and Daddy want to be alone. All of these are messages that parents are adults with a private life and a sexual life together.

In addition to expressing passionate feelings in front of your children, you can certainly be affectionate. Snuggle while you're watching TV. It can be just the two of you, or you can pull your child onto a lap and all of you cuddle while you watch TV. Swoop your child up into your arms after you passionately kiss your wife and kiss her, too, so that the three of you hug each other. When you touch or are touched, it feels good. You and your mate should touch and sometimes include your children. Affection is one of the ways families can feel good together.

You as a couple can get around the trade-offs of parenthood. You can spend time alone together, maximize privacy and spontaneity, schedule time for sex to guarantee quality erotic episodes. Owning your couple sexuality and focusing on your relationship by spending time exploring each other's changing minds and bodies give you the best of both worlds—the sensuality and richness of life parenthood offers and the happy security of an exciting relationship as experienced by nonparenting couples.

Stages of Parenting

POSTPARTUM. Ann and Aaron were looking forward to making love after their baby was born. They had discovered new ways of being sexual together during Ann's pregnancy but wanted again to look into each other's eyes while having intercourse. Ann missed feeling Aaron's penis thrusting, coming with the pressure of his penis deep inside her, their bodies pressing close.

As soon as they were given the go-ahead from her doctor, they tried to make love. But Aaron could not enter her! He felt as if he hit a wall in her vagina! Ann only felt pain. Her vagina felt like raw meat, small and tight. The pain was so intense she had to shut her eyes so that Aaron would not see her tears. "Oh, no!" Ann thought. "Suppose we never have our same old sex life. Suppose somehow the baby has ruined me. It feels as if my vagina has collapsed. Maybe some vital nerves were damaged during delivery. No one told me it would hurt so. . . . After all, my doctor said it was okay."

Aaron was disappointed, too. Even though it had been less than a month, it seemed like ages since they had made love. He wanted sex and was eager to make love to Ann's unpregnant body, feel her without a wedge between them. He knew Ann thought her vagina was smaller, but it didn't feel that way to him. Just the opposite, it felt loose and stretched out. He worried that the baby had permanently stretched her so that never again would he feel her warm moistness close around him. She felt big and gapping.

Aaron and Ann were both concerned about their sexual relationship. They had not imagined intercourse would still hurt—everything was supposed to be healed. After the first panic wore off, they decided to wait another week, and then pretend Ann was a virgin again. That sounded exciting, and they were feeling intrigued by their next sexual contact. The next week Aaron was able to enter her, but the pain was still so great Ann asked him not to continue. This was certainly more difficult than when she was a virgin!

The following week the pain was less. Aaron tried hard to control his orgasm, wanting Anne to come, but the pain again throbbed inside her and her arousal was quickly quashed. She asked Aaron to come if he could, not to worry about her orgasm. Later that night they had a long talk about their sexual relationship and devised a strategy with the goal of regaining their previous sexual relationship. "After all," they reasoned, "there must be sex after childbirth!" Their plan worked, and by the time their baby was three months old, Ann was again orgasmic through intercourse.

Some of you have no difficulty reestablishing your sexual relationship and find yourself easily getting back into your prepregnancy sexual routine. After months of pregnancy, you may look forward to having your sexual relationship return to normal immediately after your baby is born. Yet for most of you this is not to be. The postpartum period is difficult for most couples. Three months after birth, 77 percent of women are not making love as frequently as they did prior to pregnancy. Even one year after birth, 57 percent of women are making love less than they were before they got pregnant. So the postpartum period may be the first time that together you must devise a plan to overcome a sexual difficulty.

Birth may have torn the inside of your vagina, you may still be tender from your episiotomy, your muscles may have stretched as you pushed your baby out. Your vagina may be dry, and use of a lubricating jell may impair sensation. You may fear that your sexual relationship is permanently destroyed. You may worry that you will never again enjoy sex as you did before you were pregnant, that that is the price you pay for having a baby. Unfamiliar birth control may seem like a great inconvenience interrupting desire. The withdrawal of your pregnancy hormones may leave you feeling sad and inadequate in so many areas that the idea of being sexual may seem like another task. You may be exhausted, and sleep may seem like a bigger thrill than sex. But it is crucial for you to reestablish your sexual relationship. First your entire body, including your vagina, must have time to heal; and second, you must reeducate your body sexually. Many of you will find that three months postpartum you are able to enjoy sex again.

It's crucial that you take care of yourself after childbirth. You need to sleep as much as possible, eat well, and rest. Keep visitors down to a minimum and try to do as little as possible. Taking care of your baby and yourself is enough. You may be eager to get up and around, want to explore having a bellyless body, but it really is as important as your doctor and all the books tell you for you to rest and eat well. When your doctor says you may resume sexual relations, you may find these techniques helpful.

1. FOR THE MALE. Your wife's vagina may be sore for quite a while, her sexual desire at a low ebb. If it is, your patience and tenderness will be called upon. Go slow, act as if she were a virgin. Maybe it will help if she guides your penis with her hand, avoiding painful areas. Push your penis in a little at a time. At first, a few gentle movements may be all she's able to take. K-Y jelly may help to lubricate her so that you may slide more easily. Don't put any pressure on her; don't expect that she'll be able to have an orgasm.

You're not responsible for her orgasm. If she does, that's a pleasant surprise, but she may need to relearn how to be orgasmic again. Sex can be a sensual, rocking close time now. Assume she'll need a few days' rest in between attempts at intercourse. You may want to use some of the noncoital sexual skills you practiced during her pregnancy.

2. FOR THE FEMALE. It's your vagina and you may fear that you will be stretched out, sore, or too tight forever. Your baby's large head came out of your vagina—but you may be surprised to discover that your husband's penis can hardly fit in! Or the reverse may be true; you may feel as if you're a cavern. First, try to relax. Your vagina may never be quite as it was prior to birth, but you will be able to be orgasmic again. Don't expect to be able to jump right into hard, lusty sex right away. If you're breast-feeding, you may have lessened desire. Or the reverse may be true and the baby's sucking may increase your desire—but you may find you are unable to consummate.

Your desire for sex may be low. Your orgasmic floor may be stretched, torn, and pulled. It's as if your sexual apparatus has forgotten how to work, as if you must start over again teaching yourself to respond sexually. Your vagina needs some time to heal. The amount of time is dependent upon the difficulty of your birth. Perhaps you want to see your stitches or vagina with a mirror. Explore yourself, your changed vagina, find out which areas are still sore, which are healed. Start relearning how to be orgasmic, using the same methods you used when you first explored your sexuality. Masturbation is one way to again start being sexual. You may find that orgasm requires a longer time than usual, but it will reassure you that your sexual organs still respond. At first, use clitoral stimulation, as your vaginal and perianal area may still be sore. The contractions of orgasm serve two functions. First, they exercise the pelvic floor, increasing muscle strength, and second, they increase your sexual desire. This is a case of the more you do, the more you can do and want to do.

In addition to masturbation, you can help your vagina get back into shape by practicing your Kegel exercises. They also will strengthen your muscles and reeducate them on how to contract, making orgasm easier. Kegel exercises are crucial now to restore your PC muscle so it continues to function, not only to increase orgiastic potential, but also to ensure urinary continence. You can do them while you're feeding your baby. If you are breast-feeding, the baby's sucking will be stimulating uterine contractions and that can be a signal to help remind you to do them. Your little baby eats so often during the day, so you'll be getting plenty of exercise.

Meanwhile you can continue to try intercourse. Let your body be the guide; if it hurts, stop. Give yourself a few more days, a week, then try again. Until you are again orgasmic during intercourse, you can enjoy sex vicariously—i.e., let your lover come. This has the additional advantage of letting your body get used to intercourse again without pressure on you to come. The sexual motions can be slow and shallow, gentle, without hard thrusts and demanding lust. Oral-genital sex and mutual masturbation can serve as sexual outlets for you until your vagina feels completely healed. Your masturbation and Kegel exercises and your husband's gentle patience will have worked to reeducate your body. Together you will have sailed through the postpartum period.

BREAST-FEEDING. Breast-feeding is a two-edged sword, both diminishing and increasing your sexual desire. On the one hand, breast-feeding lowers your libido. If you breast-feed your baby, lactation will usually prevent ovulation. It is partially the ebb and flow of these female hormones during the menstrual cycle that create sexual desire in women. Your vagina will be less lubricated. On the other hand, many of you will find your baby's sucking on your nipple to be intensely erotic. The sucking creates uterine contractions, which pull your uterus back to its prepregnant size.

Your arousal after feeding your baby may cause some feelings of embarrassment, maybe even an uncomfortable feeling that there is something strange about you. After all, you're supposed to be merely feeding your baby, not having an erotic interlude. But nature made breast-feeding feel good to motivate you to continue to let your baby nurse and perhaps to counteract the lowered libido that accompanies nursing. So enjoy these feelings, maybe even use them in your sexual relationship with your spouse. Breast-feeding may teach you just how erotic having your nipples sucked can be. Therefore, you may react with the same arousal when your husband kisses your breasts.

You and your baby form a new couple—the nursing pair. Together you are engaged in an intimate physical relationship, one that excludes your husband, your other children. It is just you and your baby. The world recedes as you stare into each other's eyes, satisfying each other's needs. Your infant is using your nipple as a lifeline, sucking, pulling, dozing, dreaming. Your need for skin-to-skin contact and affection may be fulfilled through caring for your baby. You may find that you get so much psychological and physiological satisfaction from breast-feeding that you forget about the others in your life. Your husband may feel excluded, unwanted, and unimportant. Both of you need to remind yourselves that you have needs that cannot be met by your baby, but only by each other.

Your milk-filled breasts may take part in your sexual activities. You may want your lover to suck them, as your baby has done, so that he can produce the same intensely erotic feelings that nursing does. When you're aroused, you may find that your let-down reflex pours milk all over your bed. If your breasts are full when you have an orgasm, your milk may shoot out in liquid jets. If such a wet sexual contact doesn't appeal to you, you may wish to nurse your baby before sex. The sexual arousal that nursing has produced can be satisfied by your mate without each of you having a milky sponge bath.

Some of you may find that your nipples are tender. The idea of your husband handling them may be painful to you and you may react with a grimace if they are accidentally brushed. Wearing a bra with nursing pads will protect your nipples and catch any leaking milk.

PRESCHOOL. As a woman, your children redefine your body. Your arms are for holding babies, your hair is for them to hang on to, your breasts are for them to suck. In caring for them and caring for yourself as their mother, remember to care for yourself as a woman. This is a period of loss of narcissism, when all your other roles take a backseat to your role as mother. Books and movies have portrayed this period in the classical American pattern, eventually leading to marital disruption. The woman stays home and takes care of the children; maybe she grows fatter, immersing herself in early childhood development, security blankets, balance beams, funny new words her toddler says, the swings at the nearby park. The man puts on his work clothes and ventures forth into the outside world, forging his career. If they both work, the house may feel like a train station where scheduling the activities of family members in the main activity. They both discover they are living two different lives, which only vaguely touch on each other. Unfortunately, they have become Mother and Father, subordinating their male and female individual selves.

You don't need to fall into this pattern. Don't let this happen to you! Take your sexuality, your relationship, off the back burner. The two of you can make a conscious effort to keep your relationship and your sexual life alive during the period when your children are preschoolers. You need time alone together even if you have to schedule it. Then you will be able to devote yourself to your lover without the TV or household chores, without children demanding your attention. Maybe get dressed up and have a late night dinner for two, or go to bed as soon as the kids are asleep and have a bed picnic. Their nap time can also be used to your advantage. One thing making alone time easier now is that your children go to bed early. Take advantage of it before their increasingly late bedtimes interfere with your time alone in the evening. For now, however, you can make love in front of the fireplace at ten o'clock at night. Take trips; hire a baby-sitter and go to a motel. Nurture your sexual relationship as you nurture your children. It, too, needs to be tended and cared for right now.

ELEMENTARY SCHOOL. The loss of narcissism that accompanies caring for younger children is now gone. You, as a woman, are more separate from your children, as they are more separate from you. You switch easily from your role of mother to your role of woman. Toward the end of this period you will find your children staying up late, which interferes with your alone time together. The two of you can figure out ways to get around this, such as going to your bedroom early, leaving the kids to watch TV; arranging lunches and afternoon matinees; taking short trips. Your kids are old enough now to go off to camp, which allows you a long uninterrupted time just to be man and woman together, strengthening your relationship as a couple, able to ignore, for a while, your parenthood.

HIGH SCHOOL. Your children are away from home more and more, so you and your spouse have more alone time. Often this is a rocky period for a family, as teenagers push parents away and search for the courage to find their independent way in the world. You two may need to cling to each other, refocusing on the original couple relationship as your children leave.

When your children become adolescents, you may find yourself reluctant to pat your wife on the fanny as she cooks dinner, to blow in your husband's ear while he tosses the salad. Suddenly, displays of sexual interest, or even simple affection, may feel inappropriate to you. Even off-color jokes are met with frowns of disapproval instead of your previous hearty laughter. You know your adolescent children are watching you with eagle eyes, and you may have concerns about their sexuality. It is almost as if you were hiding your own sexuality so your blossoming children will not be reminded of theirs, lest it cause them—or you—trouble. You have become conservative. This new attitude is not going to make it easier for your children to deal with their sexuality. Instead they may feel confused or rejected. Your children are going to be struggling and/or enjoying their sexuality regardless of your behavior. Your new reticence bespeaks your own reluctance to accept your child's—and your own—sexuality.

You will probably have plenty of time alone together as your teenagers focus on relationships outside of the family. Use this time to enjoy each other and to prepare for when it is just the two of you again. Perhaps you can try new hobbies. Vacations, short weekends, or shacking up in a hotel are all ways to help reestablish life for just the two of you. You also need to continue owning your sexuality in front of your teenagers, just as you did when they were younger. You are sexual. It is still okay for you to hug and kiss in front of them. They are sexual and will soon be—hopefully appropriately—acting on their sexual feelings. It is healthy for your children's image of you and of themselves for you all to employ a frank acceptance of the fact that being sexual is part of being human.

Parenthood challenges the sexual relationship of the long-term couple. Research has indicated that children hamper the quality of the sexual relationship. Husbands, who in our society often do not have the opportunity to experience the joy of caring for children, may find parenthood burdensome. There are ways around this:

1. Remember to concentrate and cherish your man-woman relationship. You are not only father and mother.
2. Be alone together by going off on vacations or sending the children on one.
3. Take weekends, afternoon delight, shack up in a motel.
4. Schedule sex so that you can spend quality time on your lovemaking.
5. Guarantee privacy in your bedroom.
6. Own your sexuality in front of your kids. It's okay to kiss in front of them. It's okay to go off and make love in the afternoon.
7. Take it slow and easy in the postpartum period, but do spend time reestablishing your sexual relationship.
8. In the preschool period, focus on your total relationship, working on growing together and understanding each other's lives.
9. During the school-age years, own your sexuality in front of your children and enjoy each other as well as them. Your sexual relationship can sometimes be your number-one priority.

Becoming parents thrusts you and your mate into a new stage. You are two mammals reproducing the species and caring for your young in another evolutionary attempt to improve the future world. Your couple sexuality encompasses sex in its totality: love-making, lust, and reproduction. Sex is reproduction as well as eroticism. Parenting adds new sensual thrills; caring for children reawakens long forgotten memories as you experience the world afresh and anew through the eyes of your children. Your and your mate's sexuality can reflect the rekindled senses of parenthood. Your sexuality is deepened as your relationship is strengthened by the experience. Issues of privacy and spontaneity can be dealt with by remembering that you are man and woman and by making your sexual relationship a priority. Each stage your children go through presents new challenges, and you guide them through childhood as a mated pair—sexual and parental.

11

BUMPS IN A SMOOTH ROAD

It would be terrific if you could look forward to a perfect sexual relationship—a relationship in which your partner wanted to make love when you did, how you did, and for as long as you did—a mate whose sexual ebbs and flows perfectly matched your own, whose biorhythms marched to the same drummer. Obviously, even in the best of sexual matching there are snags that must be dealt with. Perhaps your mate is mourning the loss of a family member and libido is decreased. Perhaps you are preoccupied with a work problem, or the two of you are working different shifts and seem to have little time together. All these bumps are challenges for the two of you to resolve using various skills.

Every couple's sexual relationship changes over time. In the beginning, you unite with the passionate intensity of youth eager for the world and confident of your own invincibility and power. As the decades roll by, the temper of your joinings changes. You use the pleasure bond you have built, the private sexual language you have created, to join with a mature power, an easy comradeship. When you are aged, your making love takes on the rhythms of a peaceful rocking, a quiet togetherness. Yes, changes in your sexual relationship are inevitable, each phase containing its own special beauty and power and passion.

Just as changes over time are inevitable, so are periods during which your sexual relationship is not all you wish it could be. These bumps in an otherwise smooth road can be dealt with and worked through. This is when your communication skills are most severely tested and you are able to rely on the pleasure bond you have built. First, acknowledge the difficulty; second, try to figure out the reason for the problem; and third, use a strategy to deal with the problem. Naturally there are strategies that best deal with each problem.

Acknowledging the Bump

Recognizing that you and your lover are having a problem is the first step in resolving it. One of you may be aware that your sexual relationship is not what you wished it to be. Often, a sexual problem is expressed by a drop in sexual frequency. You may feel your mate is no longer attracted to you, or you may feel that there is something wrong with you as you are no longer interested in sex. You may fear that this is a permanent condition, worry that perhaps your sexual relationship is over. Together you must decide if the loss of frequency is a permanent or a temporary condition.

Sometimes the reason for lowered sexual frequency is obvious, and you both are dealing with a temporary change in your relationship. This is what happened to Eleanor after her mother's death. She and Earl made love frequently. In the beginning of their relationship they made love every night. After fifteen years of marriage, their frequency probably averaged about three or four times per week. Then, Eleanor's mother suddenly died. Eleanor was in agony. It seemed impossible to go through life without ever talking again to her mother; she knew she would always miss sharing the joys in her life with her mother. Eleanor had trouble sleeping and would jerk awake throughout the night, crying; Earl would hold her, soothe her wet hair off her forehead.

During the month after Eleanor's mother died, they did not make love. Eleanor had no interest in sex. She was involved, immersed in dealing with death. Sex seemed the affirmation of life. She wasn't ready to go on with her life yet. It was clear to both Earl and Eleanor that her lack of sexual interest was part of her mourning for her mother. And just as clearly, Earl knew what to do. He waited. He held her. He reassured her. He recognized this time for what it was—a phase that would change her, maybe change them both, but would end. He knew their sexual relationship was not over, that Eleanor would again want to affirm life and would be able to leave death behind.

Eleanor was not so sure. She could not remember ever feeling so dead inside. Even after the birth of her children, she'd been able to imagine making love again, had wanted to make love again. But this was different. Maybe she would never want sex again. She apologized to Earl for being so unavailable to him and said what they both had been thinking, that her lack of sexual interest was the result of her mother's death. Earl's acceptance and reassurance were helpful. She began to believe that when she had finished the first horrible phase of mourning, her libido would return. And slowly it did. The first time they made love, it was strange. She felt shy, almost as if she would not know what to do. But she felt soothed by the tenderness, the comfort, the togetherness inherent in sex. She was not so alone anymore. She could love her mother, mourn her mother, and allow herself the pleasure, the affirmation of life, that was part of sex for her.

Eleanor and Earl had hit a bump in their sexual relationship. They acknowledged the abrupt end of their sexual activity and recognized that a clear, precipitating event had caused the problem. Unfortunately, even recognizing that you've hit a snag can be difficult sometimes. It may be hard for you to differentiate between a problem and a permanent change. Perhaps, gradually, without even being aware of it, your sexual activity has dwindled. Now, you sometimes go months without making love. Or perhaps you still make love, but the passion is absent. It's all mechanical, only technique, and you feel as if you'd rather finish your novel or mop the kitchen floor.

This is what happened to Paul. Paul was a teacher of emotionally disturbed children. He had a small class, but the high activity level and the demand for his constant attention were draining. By the time school ended each day, he just wanted to eat dinner and sit in front of the TV. He used what little extra energy he had left to mark his students' papers, and occasionally he would attend a class, trying to learn how to help them even more. Patty, his wife, felt shut out. They had just been married five years and she felt as if they were old fogies. Work. Eat. Watch TV. Roll into bed just to begin the day all over again. Weekends were somewhat better. Paul would spend Saturday recouperating from his week, and on Saturday night they might go to a movie or visit some friends, and then make love. Paul's interest in sex had dwindled slowly throughout the years. Patty felt that once a week was just not enough.

They thought they had correctly defined the problem: Paul just had a lower sexual appetite. Patty concentrated on trying to accept the situation, while Paul questioned his masculinity. They were each struggling alone. Then came summer. There had been some recent cutbacks and for the first time in many years, Paul was not teaching. Slowly their lovemaking increased. At first neither of them noticed it, but by August they were making love three or four times a week. Patty teasingly asked, "What is there about this summer that is making you so hot?" Her comment set Paul's mind in motion. Yes, he felt sexual, alive, eager. What was there about this summer that was making him feel so sexual? Then he thought about Labor Day and school starting up again. It was almost as if he could feel his penis wilting, his passion draining out of him. He realized that his job was seriously draining his sexuality. Something about the constant pressure, the demands, the high activity level of the youngsters exhausted him so much emotionally and physically that he was not interested in sex. At last the problem had been correctly defined, and with Patty's help, he could work on resolving it.

In order to correctly recognize a snag in your sexual relationship, you need to ask yourself some questions: "Is this the way I want my sexual relationship to be?" "Is this the way my spouse wants our sexual relationship to be?" If the answer to both these questions is a resounding "No!" then you've hit a bump and you're probably not dealing with a permanent change. Then ask, "What is going on in my life, or in my spouse's life, that is diminishing our sexual relationship?"

It may be hard to tell your lover that you're unhappy with your sexual relationship. Remember how it used to be and recall that. Perhaps you can say, "It seems we used to make love so much more often; do you think this is how it's supposed to be?" Or say, "It seems we were so much more adventurous, why do you think sex is always the same now?" Your spouse's answer will certainly give you a clue as to whether you both share this concern. Talk about it. You'll never know what's going on or how to fix it unless you do. See where your partner is. See if your lover is also concerned. Once you've both agreed that you've hit a bump in your sexual relationship, you can go on to the next step and try to figure out what's causing the problem, using some of the strategies outlined here to iron out the wrinkle, so your sexual relationship is more where you both want it.

Strategies

There are many different strategies to help the two of you through a difficult sexual period. Each strategy seems best suited for a specific problem. Remember: When dealing with any problem, in addition to empathizing with your partner, you need to communicate. Talking about the problem, agreeing on ways to surmount it, trying out your ideas, and getting feedback are crucial.

WAITING. Waiting is a terrific strategy when there is a sudden sexual change following a specific event. There are a number of events that may influence sexual interest. The death of a family member is certainly one. Eleanor and Earl were faced with a drastic curtailment of sex following her mother's death. They waited. Then sex was good and plentiful once again. You may react in surprising ways to such a loss. Some of you, like Eleanor, will not be interested in sex. Others of you will feel a strong need to make love. You may want the closeness, the comfort of sex. You may need to reassure yourself that life can still hold joy. You may need to use sex as an outlet for the powerful feelings that beset you.

You may find your sexual interest also changes after you suffer a sudden psychological blow. Perhaps you've just been fired or had a heart-wrenching argument with a friend, or maybe one of your children is having trouble. Your interest in sex may also change as you channel your psychological and physical energy into solving your dilemma.

Physical problems and concerns may also create a change in sex for you. You may be worried about your health or the health of your partner, and these worries overshadow all other feelings. Temporary physical changes may make sex difficult. Maybe your wife has just given birth to a baby. Perhaps one of you has a slipped disc, mononucleosis, or another condition that lingers and saps energy. These non–life threatening illnesses need to be waited out. Your partner is not disinterested in you, simply not feeling up to par, and as soon as the physical problem is resolved will probably want to resume your usual sexual life with renewed vigor.

The fact that all of these are temporary seems obvious to an outsider, but when you're going through it, it's not always that clear. A period without sex may seem to last forever. You may feel rejected. You may feel as if your sex life is over and you'll never want to make love again. It may be the reverse—you may feel insatiable and wish to make love constantly, feel as if you've suddenly turned into a sex-obsessed person. Perhaps you fear that you cannot possibly satisfy your spouse and that you are being hounded to be sexual.

Once you make the connection between the changed behavior and the cause, the problem will feel less overwhelming. Allow yourself the psychic time to heal your wounds. You do not need to push yourself to feel an emotion. If you are feeling nonsexual, then assume all your psychic energy is focused on your problem and let yourself concentrate on getting through this period. You need to remind yourself that this, too, will pass. You will not mourn your family member forever. There must be sex after childbirth, since some families have more than one child. The flu ends and temporary physical problems do improve.

Talk about it together and then give it some time. Set a date together for when you think things should be feeling more normal. Perhaps two months after the death of his father, your husband will again feel sexual. Perhaps four months after the birth of your child, your wife will again be able to enjoy intercourse. Perhaps a few months after your spouse gets the all-clear from the doctor, you will both glory in making love.

What do you, the spouse, do? You need to be supportive, of course, and help your partner through this difficult time. Your lover may have trouble remembering that this is a phase which will end. Your confidence in the happy resumption of your sex life will be helpful. In the meantime, your spouse's disinterest does not necessarily mean you must shut down sexually. In fact, you should not. You can still fantasize about sex. You can still daydream about sex. You can still masturbate. Keep yourself sexually primed so that when sex resumes for the two of you, you can be the leader, the initiator who confidently orchestrates the opening night of a new sexual season. Your spouse will enjoy being sexual once again. Your sexual relationship will resume its previous perimeters.

OVERRIDING DAYTIME WORRIES. There may be times when the pressures of your daily life seem to swallow you up, consuming your emotions and attentions. There are times of pressure for all of us when our sense of excitement about life and our passion for sex are diminished. You may find it difficult to put your worries aside so that you can give yourself emotionally and physically to your partner. Perhaps during lovemaking you find yourself making a mental list of the tasks left unaccomplished. Maybe your mind plays over and over a conversation with your boss, or you find yourself wrestling with a concern about a child.

Sometimes this can be insidious, creeping up so that you are hardly aware of it. Slowly, as with Paul and Patty, your sexual relationship diminishes. You're not even aware that outside pressures are interfering with your lovemaking because you don't get that far. Your passion has vanished. Once you recognize this problem, there are some things you can do about it.

Paul and Patty were relieved when they realized that Paul's job was diminishing his libido. It wasn't that he had little sexual interest, it wasn't that he was bored with Patty. But now they had to make a change. Paul didn't want to change his job—in spite of its difficulty, he loved the students and felt he was making an important contribution—though he did consider this. First, they decided to see if they could change the negative effect that the job was having. Paul decided to start an exercise routine. Sure enough, after a few months of working out he found that he actually had more energy. Rather than burying his feelings of turmoil, frustration, and anger, he spent time talking about them. Every night, he would tell Patty in detail about his day. This ventilation allowed him to get rid of the tension and wash himself clean psychically so he could feel something else. Patty understood the frustration as well as his sense of accomplishment about his job. They agreed to get into bed at nine o'clock every Wednesday evening to make love, play games, and try out new sexual ideas and paraphernalia. These three things worked. They had resolved a difficulty.

You, too, may need some strategies to help you get rid of your daytime worries and tension so that you are able to give to your partner. First, talking about the day-to-day events may help. Devote time to hearing about what really happened to each other that day. You'll probably need the daily updates to fully understand your partner's working life, and it serves as a marvelous way to leave the office at the office for the rest of the night. Nonwork problems also need to be aired. Maybe you're worried about your parents or your child. Talk about it. Discuss it from all angles with your spouse. If that's not enough, talk it over with a friend.

Second, exercise can help to get rid of tension. This is also good for your body and your sexual capacities.

Third, try exchanging massages. Give your partner a massage when you realize the day has been terrible. Perhaps you can see the tension in his shoulders, the tightened brow and restricted mouth when your lover walks in that night. A back or a foot massage might be all that your lover needs so that the two of you can enjoy an evening together instead of sinking into more tension or exhaustion.

Fourth, progressive relaxation techniques are helpful in easing tension and adding vitality. Progressive relaxation techniques are muscle-relaxing exercises which many of you may have learned during childbirth preparation or if you are interested in self-hypnosis. You begin by lying down in a comfortable position in a quiet room. Then you simply start at your toes, tensing and then relaxing each set of muscles as you go up your body. Remind yourself how relaxed each set of muscles is getting. Tell yourself, "I can feel all the energy draining out of my calves, they feel limp, all the tension is gone." Spend a long time concentrating on relaxing your hands, your shoulders, your face and brow. Then take ten very slow, very deep breaths, each one lasting for a count of ten. Start at your toes again and move up your body, this time just relaxing each set of muscles.

Use phrases and images that connote good feelings and peace. Maybe you'll think about the sea and pretend you are lying in sand. At this point, you'll have put yourself in a light trance. You can suggest anything you want. You may put your worries about your job on a boat and float it out to sea or imagine how vital and alive, how full of energy you'll feel when you get up. See yourself enjoying your evening, imagine a new way to be sexual. This technique can also be used to ease you into sleep when you are tense. When you're having trouble sleeping, imagine how sleepy you're getting, so sleepy you can hardly keep your eyes open. You'll need practice to be able to use this technique successfully each time, but it is so helpful for such a wide variety of problems it's worth learning.

In addition to these four strategies to help override worries, you may have some of your own. Perhaps meditation helps to make you feel centered and eager for more experiences. Maybe a long commute home, a quiet walk around the block, or a romp with your dog sheds your tensions. If you find that you are unable to enjoy your time with your lover or muster the energy to be sexual, then use these techniques to help you.

COMPROMISE. There are times when compromise is the best solution. You might not be able to get what you want sexually all the time. Your lover might not be able to get what she wants all the time. The two of you may have to reach a compromise. Perhaps you prefer sex in the morning and your lover likes it best in the afternoon, but you only see each other in the evening. Maybe you are working different shifts and never seem to see each other when you both are feeling sexual. Maybe you'd like to make love five times a week and your lover feels once a week should suffice. Maybe you'd like to spend hours kissing and your partner wants to spend hours joined in intercourse. You are not the same; you can't be expected always to want the same things at the same time. You both need to accept that there are going to be sexual differences and figure out what to do about them.

This is what happened to Rosa and Roy. Rosa loved sex in the afternoon. She loved the daylight peeping through the drawn blinds. She felt most sexual then, awake for the day yet not tired out by it. Sex in the afternoon felt luxurious, special. Roy loved sex in the morning. Still warm from the night, aroused by his dreams, relaxed and vulnerable, he loved the coziness and closeness of sex in the morning. What a way to start the day! He felt the afternoon was for working, the nighttime for pursuing his hobbies and reading. Yet it seemed that nighttime—though it was not the favorite time for either of them—was when Rosa and Roy made love. They realized what an irony this was, since Rosa did not feel disturbed by sex in the morning before she was fully awake and Roy was not disturbed by sex in the afternoon when he felt he should be working.

In talking about it they realized they had made a compromise but wondered if they could make a better one, one in which at least one of them got it the way they really wanted it. Rosa agreed to try sex in the morning. Roy bought her a timed automatic coffee maker for the bedside table. She had a cup of coffee and then they made love. She liked it. It was different; sex in the morning had its own special charm. Roy agreed to try sex in the afternoon. That Saturday they agreed to take an afternoon siesta. Roy was impressed with Rosa's passion; he had seldom seen her quite so ardent. Afternoon was clearly her time of greatest physical power. Her passion was as a great reinforcement for afternoon delight. Sometimes they compromised the old way and made love at night, and sometimes they compromised the new way and made love in the morning or afternoon.

Compromise does not always mean meeting in the middle. You can agree to take turns getting it all your way, doing it all your lover's way. You can do this with frequency wishes, too. Perhaps you'd like to make love once a week and your partner five times. One week try meeting in the middle and making love three times, then get it your way and make love once, and then have it your partner's way and make love five times. All of these can be compromises. Compromise is the best strategy when you have differences.

THERAPY. Sometimes you may decide to try therapy. Therapy may be helpful if you are feeling in pain about your sexual relationship and everything you have tried on your own has failed. Perhaps you have had a long-standing sexual problem which has always lessened the pleasure you have received from sex. Maybe you ejaculate prematurely, or not at all; maybe you have trouble maintaining erections. Maybe you are not orgasmic or lack passion and awareness of your own arousal. In the last decade, there has been a growing body of knowledge devoted to sexuality and how to help those of you who have sexual problems.

Therapy is also helpful if you have a relationship problem that is interfering with sexuality. This would be similar to a "bump," but of longer duration; again, nothing you and your lover have tried has worked. Maybe madonna/whore issues following marriage or the birth of a baby are interfering with sex. Perhaps hidden angers, feelings of being suffocated or isolated in your relationship, are surfacing, creating sexual problems. These intimacy problems or relationship difficulties can benefit from therapy. You, or both of you, together, can find a psychologist, marriage and family counselor, clinical social worker, or sex therapist with whom you feel comfortable. Remember, as you shop for a therapist, that feeling as comfortable as possible with the therapist is very important in the positive outcome of that therapy.

SETTLING. Unfortunately, sometimes nothing works. You feel as if you've tried everything. Your sexual relationship is not what you wish it to be. This was true for Fay and Frank. They had both had many other sexual relationships when they met and fell in love. They were in their late thirties and had just about given up finding a person with whom to share their lives, so they felt a special joy when they realized they wanted to spend the rest of their lives together. Everything was terrific in their relationship. They made each other happier than they had ever been before. They glowed. Their friends all remarked that they looked years younger and reminded them what being in love was all about.

From the beginning, however, there was a fly in the ointment. The sex was never great. Both of them had had more passionate, special sexual relationships with other partners. They always thought that love could guarantee sexual thrills. But for them, it didn't. They enjoyed sex together and they loved pleasing each other, touching each other, cuddling. They were both orgasmic and loved the closeness that sex brought, the feelings they shared. Their sexual relationship was good, it was satisfying, but they didn't have that magical sexual chemistry. They could not inject that potent sexual passion in their joinings. They tried everything: talking, telling each other their fantasies, therapy, watching pornography. They were always making love to each other but were never transported into lusting. It saddened them occasionally. But the companionship, the love, the mutual interests, and the lives they were building together gave them a deep sense of peace and purpose that prior, lustier relationships had never matched. Without question or hesitation, they were more important to each other and would not consider jeopardizing what they had found together by going on a futile search for an even more perfect relationship. They knew they had "settled" for a relationship that was terrific in every way but sexually, but it did not feel that they had lost as much as they had found in each other.

Sexually, you may have grown away from each other. Together you have talked and talked about it. It's been this way for many years and you've tried everything you can think of. New positions, gadgets, and gizmos, special sexual techniques, games, therapy. You've told each other your fantasies, you've played some of them out. It's not that you don't enjoy sex together. Certainly you're both orgasmic, but it's just not special anymore. Yet the rest of the relationship seems fine. You are very close and able to talk with each other freely. You enjoy your lives together, you love raising your children together and spending time with your friends. From the outside you look like the perfect couple. You can sometimes even fool yourselves. But you both know that sexually your relationship is not what you would like it to be. The sex could be better. Sometimes that's the way it is. The chemistry isn't what you dreamed, the passion isn't as intense as it was in other relationships. But your total relationship is so great, and the love is so strong, that the lack of lust really feels okay.

You have a big decision to make and only you can make it. How important is sex to you? As with Fay and Frank, does the fact that everything else in your relationship is good outweigh the sexual dissatisfaction? Or does it feel that nothing is really right if the sex isn't more passionate? Sex is only one part of your life and only one part of a couple's relationship. The two of you may decide that your life together is so important, that so many other needs are being met, that you're willing to live without terrific sex. You would not want to lose the relationship. This certainly is a legitimate and honored decision. You are not compelled to have the best sexual relationship possible at the sacrifice of everything else. However, you may decide that the bitterness and disappointment about sex would tarnish the rest of your relationship. You make great friends and companions, but lousy lovers. This decision, too, is up to you. No one can dictate how important sex should be. Sometimes you have to decide whether you are going to settle. And if you decide to settle, settle joyously.

Special Problems

You may unfortunately run across some problems that create some special difficulties for you as a couple. Some of these all of us must deal with—we all must deal with fertility problems; we all must deal with the sexual changes aging brings. Some of us must also deal with infidelity and the impact that has on our sense of sexual trust. And unfortunately, some of us must deal with illness.

These are sad or tragic aspects of life, the rain, or torrents, that we all suffer. Yet we are able to continue living, to enjoy and share sexuality.

FERTILITY: BIRTH CONTROL. Too bad we can't blithely enjoy sex without a care about consequences and then, then we decide we want to have a baby, push some magic button and instantly get pregnant! Without a doubt, worry-free, barrier-free sex, with naked organs pushing against naked organs, feeling the natural skin and folds and fluids, is the best. Unfortunately, it doesn't work that way and until you reach menopause or one of you is sterilized, you must either deal with the inconvenience of birth control or the sadness of infertility. Both impact on sexuality. There has not yet been a device invented that has no side effects and that does not interfere with sex. The pill and the IUD, both greeted as the perfect solution to this problem, have side effects. The barrier devices—condoms, diaphragm, the new cervical cap and sponge—may feel inconvenient to you or may impair sensation. As inconvenient and annoying as this is, the problems from an unwanted pregnancy are much worse.

As a couple, you need to resolve this issue. If your form of birth control negatively impacts on your sexual relationship, then your pleasure and sexual frequency will decrease. Perhaps you feel like making love in the middle of the night but hate the idea of getting out from under the warm covers and into the cold night air to fumble around in the dark to locate your diaphragm. So instead of acting on your feelings, you roll over and go to sleep. Perhaps the condom diminishes sensation. When you're young you may find this a useful tool, as it helps you increase your "staying power"; but as a mature man, you may find the decrease of sensation a severe destructor of pleasure. Perhaps you worry so about the pill or IUD that you fear you're reaping pleasure today to pay with much pain tomorrow. This is an important couple sexual problem. Together you need to figure out solutions.

You may use different forms of birth control at different stages in your life. You need to feel comfortable with your physician in working out the best form of birth control given your medical history and your concerns and wishes. The pill may be the answer for you if you are young, don't smoke, and there is no history of heart disease in your family. Barrier devices can be used following the birth of a child. An IUD may be used in between children, when you've finished nursing your baby. You may decide for one of you to be sterilized when your family is complete.

The pill and the IUD are two birth-control measures that will not interfere with lovemaking. If you need to use a barrier device, experiment with the different types. Many of you may have difficulty with the condom. It may impair sensation, it may necessitate a jell. Try out the new generation of condoms, which are much superior—thinner, some with ribs, some with lubrication. You may need to order some of these from a catalogue. Perhaps for you the diaphragm, the cervical cap, or the sponge interferes very little with sexuality. Your husband may not feel it at all, and you may not, either. In that case simply put it in before intercourse and it will not interfere with your sexual contact at all. This may not be true for all of you, however. Perhaps the diaphragm seems to decrease vaginal sensation. It could be that it prevents your G-spot from being directly massaged. Perhaps the cord of the sponge irritates the glans of your husband's penis. Maybe barrier techniques worked well for you when you were young, but now, after experiencing the joy of sex without barriers, the devices hamper you. Maybe you use a variety of techniques—the rhythm method with the aid of a temperature chart and a barrier device when you are most fertile. Perhaps you trade off, sometimes using a condom and sometimes using a sponge or diaphragm.

Regardless of what method you use, it must be the most satisfactory method for you as a couple. The great majority of you decide, when your family is complete, to get sterilized. This gives you, at last, complete sexual freedom—no worry, no inconvenience. The decision to be sterilized is a serious one. A vasectomy—the sterilization of the male by cutting the vas deferens, which carry the sperm into the penis—is the simplest form. However, many of you may fear that such an operation will hamper your sexuality. In your head you know it's a sterilization, but you fear it will make you impotent. You may joke that the doctor is cutting your penis. Sort these feelings out before you have the surgery. You need to feel completely confident that your sexual potency is not tied up with your sperm count.

You may find that there are periods in your life when birth control hampers the freedom and simple joy of lovemaking. Together you must experiment and explore, continue to work with your physician while science makes advances in this area.

INFERTILITY. The idea of barrier-free, side-effect-free, pregnancy-free sex may be so entrancing that those of you who have a problem with birth control may sometimes envy those whose problem is the opposite—infertility. Of course those who are infertile would gladly change places. Infertility, too, hampers sexuality. First, it hampers it psychologically. Many of you, when you fell in love, talked and dreamed and yearned for the product of your love, your joining. A child is the proof, the continuation of that love. Unfortunately, one out of five of you will have to deal with the problem of infertility at some point. You may feel sad. You may feel as if sexually you were not really meant to be joined. The anger you feel at your body's betrayal may be transferred to the sexual act itself. You may find yourself withdrawing or distancing yourself. You may punish yourself or your spouse by withholding your own responsiveness. You may act out your anger by not giving your lover pleasure.

Additionally, the tests, the machinations you both go through during fertility testing, and trying to get pregnant, can interfere with your sexuality. This is what happened to Daphne and Don. Daphne longed to get pregnant. All she ever wanted was to be a mother. When she married Don, she envisioned him as the perfect father, loving and gentle, nurturing. Children and family were extremely important to them both. They planned their future together around children yet to be. Daphne went off the pill with such joy, imagining that within a year she'd be cuddling a babe to her breast. And then nothing. Each month when she felt her breasts swell and become tender, her hopes soared. Her breasts were getting ready for her baby, she thought. Then, each month when she saw her red-spotted panties, her spirits plummeted. Again. Another month. What irony, especially when her best friend was overwhelmed and complaining about having had three children in under four years. Life had dealt her a severe blow.

Then she and Don started their rounds of tests. She had air blown through her tubes to make sure they weren't blocked. She had the lining of her uterus scraped to make sure her hormones were functioning. Don's sperm was checked and rechecked. And every morning she took her temperature, plotting it on a chart. Daphne's early-morning temperature fluctuated with her hormones, indicating by its valleys and mountains when she was ovulating, when would be the most likely time for conception. The chart dictated their sexual relationship. They made love when the chart and the doctor said they should, not when they felt like it. They couldn't make love too often or Don's sperm count would decrease. They watched the chart. It told them when they must feel, when they must act on those feelings. They found they were beginning to resent the whole process. Sex wasn't fun anymore. It was something you did on a certain day, in a certain position, for what always became a futile dream. Don and Daphne realized that their sexual relationship, which had always been the backbone of their marriage, was disintegrating. They realized they had to do something quickly.

There are some things you can do to help yourselves through this period. You've got to keep talking. If you can share your deep disappointment and sadness, your fears and feelings of inadequacy about struggling to reproduce a child, then you won't feel so alone. It is a couple problem, and you as a couple can figure out what to do. The period when you are trying to get pregnant and "the chart" is dictating your sexual relationship may be the most difficult one sexually. Sex may seem to be only for reproduction—and your feelings about your infertility may be so great that responsiveness is hard.

Try to separate lovemaking, reproductive sex, pregnancy, and parenthood. Try to see these as separate, not necessarily lying on a continuum, not necessarily steps. Sex does not have to lead to pregnancy. You may need to set aside some time to be sexual in your old way. Have an orgy of lovemaking before, during, and after your period, when you are unlikely to conceive but there will still be time for your husband to build up his sperm count. Maybe for a month ignore the chart. Give yourselves a vacation from the pressure of trying to get pregnant. If the making love "for a baby" is becoming burdensome to you, then forget the making-love part. Focus on the reproductive part. Don't expect it to be terrific lovemaking, passionate and intense. It's okay to do it just for the baby. Later that night, maybe you'll want to express your sexual and loving feelings for each other with your bodies. Remember, too, you've enjoyed making love when it had nothing to do with pregnancy, before you started trying to get pregnant.

You may need to help each other through some of the newer scientific ways to get pregnant. There are many different strategies that can be used to help infertile couples—both chemically and surgically. You can also become parents without pregnancy and childbirth, through adoption. Regardless of which options are possible for you, regardless of how you decide to form your family, distinguish reproductive sex from making-love sex, or lusting sex. This keeps your basic lifelong sexual relationship—the passion, the making love, the lusting—apart from the physical requirements and difficulties of reproduction. It is the reproductive aspect of sex that is the problem, not the passionate, lusting, loving desire. Hold on to that. Remember.

INFIDELITY. Some of you may be sexually unfaithful to your spouses. You may feel as if the sexual compact, the closeness, and the intensity are smashed. You may feel that you never again will feel sexually special, one with each other. A third person has intervened. A third person has shared your lover's body. Someone else hangs over your marriage bed like a specter, keeping you from losing yourselves in each other.

Infidelity can be caused by many different reasons, some of them having to do with problems within your relationship, and some a result of individual internal turmoil. For some of you, it may signal the end of your relationship. Maybe you have grown so far away from each other that there is little basis for meeting. For others, it may act as a red flag, alerting you to the fact that you both have work to do on your relationship. Perhaps you have not been communicating and sharing your lives, so you feel misunderstood. It could be that you are needing more emotional intensity. Maybe you have allowed your sexual relationship to become mundane and unexciting. For others, infidelity may be an attempt to resolve a problem with which one of you is struggling. Perhaps you need reassurance that you are attractive and appealing to others. As you struggle with midlife changes, you may seek the ego gratification of seducing someone. Look at the reasons for infidelity and then decide how you are going to handle it.

Some of you will decide that it means the end of your relationship. It is not so much that the "other person" has broken up your relationship; rather, it is an indication of a relationship already over. Many of you will be able to go on with your relationship, looking at what the extramarital affair means and resolving the difficulties. Regardless of whether your affair is caused by a relationship problem or an individual problem, it may impact on your sexual relationship. This is what happened to John and Janice. There were both in their late twenties and had been married for seven years. When it was all over they joked that they must have had the "seven-year itch." But they never thought they would joke about it when Janice first found out that John was having an affair. She felt betrayed. Furious. Enraged. Tricked. How could he do this to her? She felt sad and vulnerable—almost guilty, as if somehow she had been responsible. She must have done something wrong. She must not have been enough for him. In one week she dropped ten pounds. She couldn't eat or sleep. She cried and raged the entire week.

John felt scared. An affair was one thing, but he did not envision losing his wife! It was just a little diversion to him. A month-long stand. Seduced by and seducing a woman with whom he worked. He had desperately needed some sort of psychological lift, and this woman had provided it. His career was going nowhere, and he was at a vocational crossroads after several disappointments. Janice loved her work and was accumulating promotions and pay raises.

He felt alone and somehow not enough of a man in his marriage. For a while, the affair had restored his self-confidence.

Janice and John talked and talked. Janice could understand why John needed the affair. She was able to forgive him but knew she could never forget. Moreover, she was afraid that she would never again feel secure with him sexually. The intensity of their feelings for each other diminished; he had taken his sexual feelings elsewhere. No longer was he only hers. She had trouble letting him touch her, imagining his hands on the other woman's body, his penis inside the other woman's vagina. It had all been tarnished.

If you discover that your lover has had an affair, you, too, may feel as though the bonds in your sexual relationship have been severed. This is because one of you has created a distance. By sleeping with another, you take your sexual, and perhaps emotional, feelings to another to share. You diminish the transferential intensity of your primary relationship. This creates a distance in the spousal relationship. You will need to rebuild the sexual intensity and closeness.

If you're the one who was unfaithful, you, too, may feel sexually seared. You, too, may have images you wish to blot out and replace with images of your spouse. You, too, may deeply regret your behavior and need help reconnecting with your spouse. This is something for both of you to remember as you go through this period. You are *both* hurting. You both may wish to reunite and recommit sexually.

REUNITING TECHNIQUES. These can be used to reestablish the intensity of your sexual relationship. They can also be used whenever there is a serious rent in your relationship—such as after a big fight, separation, illness, or period of emotional and sexual differences.

First, you need to talk and listen. Take turns at this. Talk, yell, cry, sob out your feelings. Let your lover know the depth of your hurt and pain. Share your core soul. As you talk and share your feelings, you may learn the reasons why you feel as you do, you may learn why you behaved as you did. Then you listen. As you listen, you have an equally arduous task. You hear, you try to understand, you do not interrupt or defend. You need to know how your partner feels, and you need to accept how your partner feels. As you talk and listen, you will slowly begin to feel close again. By sharing your feelings you are being vulnerable to your lover. By listening, you are accepting. You see and feel the situation from your lover's view, you explore the situation from your view.

Second, get reacquainted physically. Take it slow. It may feel scary, you may feel shy, you may feel inept, afraid to move too fast or slow. Start with nonsexual physical closeness. Holding and comforting each other from the pain you have caused. Soft, gentle, nonpressuring kisses. Then try nongenital touching with your clothes on, then nude genital touching. Take it slow and start from the beginning again.

Third, spend time together, do things together. Do the ordinary things that you used to like to share. Maybe you'll take a walk or go to a movie, any activity that reaffirms the two of you as an ordinary couple being comfortable together, going on with your couplehood.

Fourth, be sexual again. You may need to talk as you go. Ask questions. Perhaps you feel you really do need to know what your partner did sexually with the other person. Maybe you feel in knowing what they did together, you're not so left out, excluded. Maybe knowing what they did creates vivid, unpleasant images in your mind. Perhaps imagining is worse for you. You need to figure this out for yourself and act accordingly.

Making love the first time is bound to be bittersweet. You will feel relieved that you can still unite. You may need to cry over the loss. But being together again will reassure you that you can still make love, can still share something special. It's not going to feel like you are brand-new lovers again embarking on a new voyage, but rather lovers who know more about each other, understand more about each other. After the first few times, you will be able to rely on the pleasure bond you had built before the incident. The years you shared before the affair, the years you will share after the affair, dwarf the importance of it. As time goes on, you may gain a different perspective, as something one of you, or both of you, needed to do a long time ago. You are stronger together. Your relationship may not be inviolable, but it cannot be destroyed. It is solid.

ILLNESS. As you go through life, the two of you may have to face illness, which impacts on your sexual relationship. Loss of libido may accompany almost any illness. Many of us do not feel like making love when fighting a lingering cold or recovering from a virus. In this case, you merely wait for your lover to get better and then resume your sexual relationship. There are illnesses that will have a more serious impact on your sexual relationship. Some create temporary sexual problems and some involve permanent sexual changes.

Perhaps you have just had a mastectomy. You feel scared about your health, you feel a sense of loss over your missing breast, you feel unsure about your sexuality. You may feel anxious about your husband's reaction to your changed body. Maybe you've had a colostomy or other surgery that changes your body. Any surgery that changes the external shape of your body is going to impact, to some degree, on your sexual relationship. In this case, you can use the techniques mentioned above regarding reuniting to talk about your feelings. Both of you may have clusters of general and sexual fears. Share these and then slowly reunite.

Carol and Cam had a serious accident that changed their lives as well as their sexual relationship. They were horseback riding when Cam's horse was stung by a bee and took off at a terrifying gallop. The horse ran close to a tree, knocking Cam to the ground, unconscious. He was in a coma for several days. When he woke up he was a different person. He seemed to be twelve again. He did not remember Carol or their children. He did not remember the life they had built together. He had trouble concentrating and was unable even to read or follow a TV program. He was exhausted all the time. One small chore would send him to bed for the rest of the day. He was depressed. Needless to say, with all this going on, sex was put on the back burner for a long time. Cam was not impotent, just totally disinterested.

Cam had a long, hard road to travel before sex was even a consideration. His physical condition and poor coordination, plus his depression, made sex impossible. It was a year before Cam was able to even think about sex. Meanwhile, Carol was also suffering. Cam was a different person. Would he ever be the same? What would he be like when he was all better? Would she be able to love the person he would be then? She desperately needed to be held. She wanted someone to make life all right for her again. Why had this happened to her? What was she being punished for?

Carol held Cam and rocked him as if he were the child that he appeared to be; she cuddled with him, trying to soothe them both. Eventually, as Cam was able to get his life back on track, he was able to be sexual again, and Carol had learned to love and care about the new Cam as well as rejoicing in increasing evidences of his old personality. A year after the accident, they tried making love. It was sweet, as if they had never done it before. Truly for Cam it seemed a new experience. No, it was not like before the accident. It was different. Cam was different. Carol was different, too. The sex was not better or worse—just different.

As with Carol and Cam, there are health problems that do not change the surface of the body but may impact on your sexual relationship. Maybe you've just had a heart attack or coronary bypass surgery and are terrified that sex might kill you. Maybe you have high blood pressure or diabetes, and the disease and medication interfere with your erections. Maybe you have a progressive neurological disease and you know that sex will get more and more difficult. Maybe your spouse has just had a stroke or other serious brain damage, and sex is out of the question for a long time. All of these are tragedies and sorrows that impact on your total relationship. Sex is but one small part of this, but it is a part that needs attention, too.

What do you do if such a thing happens to you and your spouse? First, remember: If you have just gone through a major illness, it impacts on both of you. It is all too easy to focus on the patient as the only one who is hurting. Yes, if you are facing a serious illness, your pain, your agony is immense. You may well be worried about yourself, fearful of your future, and trying hard to combat your illness. The attention of your friends and family may be focused on you. But your spouse is hurting, too. Your loss is your spouse's loss, also. Your partner has feelings of empathy and concern for you, as well as feelings about what it means for your relationship and for his or her life. It isn't something that you are enduring alone. You are suffering through this period together.

Second, you need to work with a doctor with whom you can discuss the sexual as well as the total impact. If you're afraid to talk with your doctor about sex, figure out why. If there is something about that particular doctor that makes you uncomfortable, get another doctor. If you are too embarrassed or shy to discuss your difficulty, then work on changing your attitude. This is too important an area to be neglected. Don't forget, your doctor is your employee; he or she is there to help you. Your doctor can be of great help. Maybe your blood-pressure medication is interfering with your erections. Your physician may be able to switch you to a medication that does not create this problem. Maybe you are left impotent as a result of illness or surgery. There are inflatable penile implants that will give you an erection so that you can perform intercourse. Maybe your vaginal walls seem to have collapsed after the birth of your last child and your spouse is unable to feel you. There are exercises and surgery that can correct this problem. Your doctor can tell you when it is safe for you to have sex if you have a heart condition. But your doctor can't help you if you don't discuss the problem.

Third, you and your spouse are going to need to experiment about what you can and cannot do. Sex does not always have to end in intercourse or orgasm. You may need to redefine your sexual relationship or learn new ways to give each other pleasure. Regardless of illness, you will be able to continue to be close together. Perhaps you spend more time cuddling, or have oral-genital contact. Maybe you enjoy taking turns with some of the gadgets and gizmos described earlier.

There are specific suggestions that are helpful for various illnesses.

HEART ATTACK. Almost 20 percent of you will have to deal with regaining health following a heart attack. Many of you will fear that your sex life is over, terrified that you may have another heart attack while making love. However, the amount of energy expended during intercourse is about the same as walking up two flights of stairs or scrubbing a floor. You can treat sex the same way you would any brief exercise. Most couples can resume sexual relations eight to twelve weeks following a heart attack, but you should check this out with your doctor. Here are some additional guidelines:

1. You should be in usual surroundings, with a comfortable room temperature. Avoid extremes of temperature—no hot or cold baths, which affect circulation. Rest before intercourse; morning is a good time. If you are likely to have angina pain, taking nitroglycerin prior to making love may be a good idea. Make love with your long-term mate; extramarital affairs add increased stress.
2. Do not make love after you have eaten or had alcohol. Wait three hours.
3. Foreplay will gradually prepare the heart for increased activity.
4. Positions for intercourse should be relaxing and permit unrestricted breathing. In the missionary position, the cardiac patient should be on the bottom. Side and sitting positions are ideal.
5. If you are wearing clothing, make sure it is loose-fitting.
6. Oral-genital sex places no undue strain on your heart. But anal intercourse, which stimulates the rectal muscle and mucus lining, should be cleared with your doctor, as it adds stress on the heart.

ARTHRITIS. Although arthritis does not directly affect your capacity for sexual excitement and satisfaction, the pain and the depression associated with the disease may impede your sexual relationship. Yet sex is good for patients with arthritis; it helps to counteract the depression. There are some things you can do to make sex easier:

1. Try to make love in the middle of the day, after morning stiffness is gone and before you are tired. Take a pain pill—or an alcoholic drink. A warm shower will also help relieve pain and stiffness.

2. Find a position that is comfortable. A woman with arthritis may have difficulty making love when she has to bend her knees or spread her legs. A man may not be able to support his weight on his hands and knees. Rear entry and side lying positions may be comfortable.
3. Alternate forms of sex, such as oral-genital, and use of gadgets and gizmos may also be helpful.

IMPOTENCE. Maybe surgery or an illness has left you impotent. There are several things you can do about this. You can continue to satisfy your wife sexually without intercourse. Or if intercourse seems very important to you both, there are ways to continue without an erection. Perhaps you place your penis in a dildo that is strapped around your body. Maybe you decide to get one of the new penile implants so you can have intercourse with your erect penis. Perhaps you learn to "stuff" your soft penis into your wife's vagina. Then, by thrusting her hips and using the muscles of her vagina, she can draw it farther in.

Regardless of your situation, sexuality is possible for you. You may need to do some research on what other couples in your physical circumstances have been able to discover. Find out from your physician what is possible for you. Then try out new ways of being sexual. It may be that parts of your sexual relationship have come to an end, but you can continue to get pleasure and give pleasure by learning or enlarging your emphasis on other parts.

AGING. As you age, there may be changes in your sexual abilities. Just as your entire body is slowing down, so are your sexual responses. If you've had a high sex drive as a youth, and have an active and regular sex life as an adult, you will be able to maintain your sexual capacity as you age. You probably can't run a seven-minute mile anymore, and you may have difficulty making love every night. But if you have been practicing running a mile, you will still be able to run one—it may be a fifteen-minute mile. By the same token, if you have been having sex regularly, barring illness, you will continue to be sexual. It's true: if you don't use it, you'll lose it. But even if you continue to use it, it will change as you age.

These changes occur in several areas. As a man, you will need a longer time between sexual contacts. Luckily, coinciding with this, you'll want sex less. Your erection may be delayed and you may not become fully hard until you are closer to orgasm. You can compensate for this by longer foreplay, or by stuffing your semierect penis into your partner's vagina. The preejaculatory stage will last longer. You may not feel the need to ejaculate but will feel satisfied by your spouse's orgasm. Your orgasm may be shorter in duration and lack the ejaculatory urgency, have less expulsive force and volume. But the feeling of intensity during climax continues. There may be a longer refractory period. You may enjoy less active positions, use imagery and fantasy rather than touch for arousal.

As a woman, you may find your vaginal walls are dry. Just as your husband is slower to erect, you may be slower to lubricate. You may wish to use a lubricating gel or estrogen cream if intercourse is painful. In addition, there is decreased elasticity of the vaginal walls. The orgasmic phase is shortened, and occasionally you may find that uterine contractions are spasmodic and painful. Clitoral sensation may be enhanced, and your orgasm feels as intense as ever. You may rely more on touch and less on fantasy for arousal.

These are the changes of aging. If you maintain your sexual life, you can continue to be sexual. You can still share your sexuality, expressing the love that you feel for each other through your bodies. There is some indication that continued sexual activity and enjoyment may have a positive effect on health. The majority of married men and women remain sexually active; even over seventy years of age a slight majority continue to have sex at least once a week. Such continued enjoyment of sex is dramatic evidence of the joy of sex and the strength of the pleasure bond. It doesn't get boring.

It is when your sexual relationship encounters problems that your communication skills, the ability to talk about sex, and the years of lovemaking pay off. Use these skills to resolve the difficulty.

1. Learn when to wait out problems.
2. When worries and stresses are diminishing your libido, talk with

your spouse, exercise to get rid of tension, exchange massages with your spouse, and use progressive relaxation techniques to invigorate yourself.

3. Compromise both by meeting halfway and by doing it first your way and then your lover's way.
4. If, in spite of everything you and your partner have tried, you are still having difficulties, go into therapy.
5. Use the least bothersome birth control method for you.
6. Use reuniting techniques after a hiatus in your relationship. Talk. Listen. Use nongenital stroking and kissing. Take it slow.
7. Sex is a part of humanity from birth until death. Don't let chronic illness prevent sexuality. Find out from your physician and through experimentation ways to assure pleasure for both of you.

Regardless of the bumps that jostle the two of you as you travel on life's road, you can continue to enjoy your sexuality. There may come a time when you need to wait for your spouse to feel sexual, there may be differences that will require a compromise. You may need to schedule time so that you can open up to each other. Fertility problems and infidelity may impede your progress—you need to find your way around these road blocks before you can continue on your journey. Illness and aging may change the way you relate to each other. All are challenges you can meet head on. By talking about your feelings, by experimenting with new techniques, you can continue to glory in your physical relationship.

12

AFTERGLOW

Katherine and Kevin were in their twenties when they met during the Depression. They fell passionately in love and after a year of knowing each other consummated their relationship. They knew it would be a long time before they got married, and they both wanted to act on the powerful feelings surging between them; so despite concerns about pregnancy, in spite of Katherine's fears that Kevin might stop "respecting" her, they made love. She wasn't certain what she was supposed to do or what was supposed to happen. Kevin was only slightly less naive than she, but they had both masturbated and knew a lot about their own bodies.

The sex was better than she had imagined. At first it hurt and felt uncomfortable, but she was surprised at how quickly she got into the swing of it. "Why, it was like dancing, but closer than ever," she thought. Kevin was a considerate and passionate lover; his desires matched hers. They would go to a hotel or one of their homes and spend hours making love. No one knew that they were lovers. It was their secret. Katherine never talked with her friends about sex, and she was sure all of them were virgins. Kevin was thrilled by his find. Here he had a woman who was a delight to spend time with and ardent as well. He treasured her, and their sexual passion cemented his affections, bound him to her.

Sexually they were well matched. What a joy it was to explore each other's bodies! Katherine had never felt comfortable with a man nude before, and she was amazed at Kevin's penis, amazed at how it would stand at attention when erect. She wondered what it would feel like to have one. Kevin was moved by the gentle curves of Katherine's body, the soft coolness of her skin, the triangle of pubic hair pointing to the mystery of her opening. They touched and looked and tasted and explored, becoming ever more daring, ever more comfortable. They had never felt such electric emotions. They were encompassed by a world they had created with their bodies.

Their sexual psyches met and meshed. They melded, transported in an enchantment they created. Katherine loved to feel him deep inside her, truly joined into one animal; and Kevin's entire body felt at home when he entered her, united and moving together. They loved doing the same things together. Long, soul-searching kisses, tentatively then forcefully entering each other's mouths with their tongues. Lying side by side, they loved to circle their sexual organs with their mouths. They stared into each other's eyes while they joined and watched the sudden expression of ecstasy, looking almost like agony, cross each other's faces.

Their bodies moved to similar rhythms, Katherine arching to pull him into her with several motions to his one long one. Kevin loved her breasts, loved nestling his head in between them, sucking on her nipples. Kevin defined Katherine's breasts for her and taught her how much pleasure they could give. Katherine taught Kevin the sensuousness of velvet tenderness. What they had learned from each other became as pleasurable as what they had instinctively done. They did not know how they had chosen so well. They did not know how they could have possibly done it so right; it was as if they had always been waiting for each other. They knew things about each other instinctively; they even shared déjà vu experiences together. How had they known beforehand that they had found the perfect partner—the complement, the piece to their puzzle?

They were sure that no lovers ever felt such ecstasy, that no man and woman ever gave each other such pleasure. No other couple was so perfectly matched, so in tune, so ardent. They were like primal man and woman discovering sex for the first time. They were even more impressed when they considered that these potent feelings could create another human being. They could hardly wait to see the product of their passion and wondered how their child would look.

They got married and discovered the joys of making love as much as they wanted whenever they wanted. No more sneaking into hotels, no more quiet sex in their houses. It was terrific; they rubbed each other raw with the quantity and lustiness of their passion. Making love was the focus of their day.

Then the war broke out and Kevin was sent overseas, flying transport planes in the Orient. When they met again they had both changed. Katherine was relieved that he had come back to her in one piece; all else was irrelevant. They were shy with each other. Katherine was afraid she had forgotten how to make love, her body had forgotten how to respond. Kevin felt tender and uncertain. He was filled with stories he had heard from his buddies in the war. New positions, new gimmicks, vaginal tricks, and different ways of moving. It was like a wedding night for both of them. Kevin shared what he had learned, and Katherine, figuring that what they could do in the Orient she could do in the USA, discovered her sexual muscles. Her orgasms became deeper than ever. Kevin had heard his friends talk about having intercourse for thirty minutes or more. He concentrated on control, prolonging his pleasure and enhancing Katherine's.

Then Katherine became pregnant, and pregnant once again. Those years during which it seemed Katherine was either pregnant, recovering, nursing, or exhausted from running after preschoolers seemed interminable to Kevin. Katherine seemed more interested in the children than in him, she seemed more interested in her own body than in his. Sex became routine. The quantity was still there, but they were both aware that the quality was lacking. It seemed ironic that the product of their lust for each other would damage the passion that produced it. Kevin joked that if they hadn't had those years before the children, he wouldn't know she was really a hot mama, but just a mama.

When their financial situation improved, they left the children with their grandparents and went off on a vacation. A week alone at Atlantic City, basking in the sun, strolling on the Boardwalk, looking at the shops. Nothing but each other. Sun and talk and swim and sex. The week-long vacation revitalized their entire sexual relationship. They took sexual risks they never had before. They talked, told each other their fantasies, the special things they would like to try. One night they made love in the sea, and once they spent the entire day ringing for room service and enjoying a long bed picnic.

Afterward, they realized how much their day-to-day life was interfering with their sexual relationship. Kevin especially felt somehow alone. Katherine got a lot of physical pleasure from her relationship with the children. He, too, loved giving them baths, feeling their little heads nestle under his chin and their little hands cling to him. But Katherine was their prime caretaker; her sexuality and needs for physical affection were sublimated by her nurturing of the children. He needed more affection. They knew that sex couldn't always be the number-one priority, but they needed to devote more time and energy to it. Somehow, in spite of worries about their jobs, the kids, the household chores, bills, schools, and their own parents, they needed time to play sexually. Sex between them was too good and too much fun to become relegated to simple body rubbing, product-oriented orgasm. They vowed to get off alone together, if only for a weekend once or twice a year, and to turn in early a few nights a month.

Before they knew it they were in their forties. The children, who, it seemed, had been toddling in diapers a few years before, were in their teens. Katherine was somehow feeling more sexual and Kevin was fearing he couldn't keep up, though he always did. Katherine always thought that sexual frequency was like breast-feeding in that it seemed regulated by some unseen supply and demand. Generally, they wanted sex about the same amount. When Katherine wanted to make love more often, Kevin's eagerness slowly grew. When one of them wanted sex less often, the frequency diminished until they were both satisfied.

Then there were rough years. Their teenagers began to rebel; Katherine and Kevin worried, and the pressure affected their libidos. Their parents died, and the mourning process further diminished their sexual relationship. Sometimes they went for months without making love—waiting, trying to help each other through the rough spots, talking, and taking long walks together. Then, more suddenly than it started, it stopped. Their house was quiet. Their kids were grown. They were alone—at last. Back to the beginning, just the two of them. They heaved a sigh of relief and learned to be just a couple again. A man and a woman.

Those were terrific years. They had all the closeness and oneness of their premarital and early marriage days, but with a quieter intimacy, a knowledge of each other and themselves born of the decades of living together. Their work made them feel productive and wise, as they nurtured the young people in their fields. They enjoyed seeing their grandchildren grow. Sex wasn't the wild, intense lust of their youth. It was calmer, deeper. Sometimes the joining was enough and they stopped short of orgasm, holding each other close throughout the night. This pattern continued through retirement, after which they had more time together. They joined a senior citizens' club and traveled, seeing sights they had only dreamed of from pictures in *National Geographic.*

Of course, they still made love—slowly, their passion easy and sure. They realized they were more adventurous than ever. Maybe it was the sexual revolution or the fact that they were keenly aware of mortality and wanted to experience as much as possible. They tried things together that would have shocked them twenty years before: pornography, anal play, body massage. Katherine thought that Kevin looked distinguished using a cane as a result of an old high school football injury. Kevin was amazed that Katherine's firm body had suddenly gone to soft wrinkles and folds. Where had all the time gone? When had she stopped being the young woman and evolved to the matron? Somehow he had always imagined her in her twenties, when they would sneak off to hotel rooms, sure they were the only couple in the world who ever felt such passion, the only couple in the world who were making love and lusting. It seemed that at each stage of their lives they were discovering a new aspect of sex. They were a couple who had invented sex.

You and your lover, too, are reinventing sex. Your sexual relationship is for you. You forge it from the furnace of your psyches, each of you bringing to it your sexuality and tempering it into a unique product that continues to evolve. It is an expression of both the deepest part of you and the relationship you share together. There is an unconscious connection, just as there is a physical joining, that builds a pleasure bond. You need to be able to talk about what you require and yearn from life, and you need to be able to talk about sex. You learn together to say what pleases you most, what you would like to try, your fantasies. You learn to own and allow your sexuality, to appreciate and glory in your lover's sexuality. By doing so, you reinforce and strengthen your relationship. Together, in your moments of passion and lust, you build a sexual language, a pleasure bond guaranteeing increasingly easy satisfaction.

As the years go by, your sexual relationship will evolve. Children may diminish the spontaneity and time you devote to sex. Illness, worries, and problems may act as snags. When you experience these bumps, your sexual relationship and the communication you have developed are tested. It is at these times you need to explore your feelings and figure out strategies, try new sexual techniques. Here, too, the pair bond you have nurtured can be relied on. Periods when sex recedes in importance make possible times of resurgence and renewal. And your bodies will change. You may have increased ease with orgasm, and it may feel that the location and type of your orgasm has changed. Keeping yourself sexually fit with exercises will ensure your continued sexual abilities. Together you define what sex will be for you; you create your own unique sexual style and limits. Sharing childbirth and nursing may make you both more comfortable with your bodies and spur creativity and exploration. You may wish to explore new sexual horizons—games, dancing, or playing out fantasies. You may enjoy trying out vibrators or seeing your response to pornography. As you age, you may find the feelings you express by sex taking precedent over the ends of sex, relishing the togetherness, the give and take and communication exchanged between you.

Your sexual relationship is part of your total relationship. And, as a long-term couple, you share all of your sexuality with each other; you explore eroticism and reproduction. You may experience pregnancy, birth, breast-feeding, lusting, making love, fantasies, the changing of your bodies over time. Your sexuality is interwoven with the fabric of your very being, making it an inextricable part of your couplehood. Making love is there for the two of you to enjoy, to explore. It brings you close, joins you together. From your sexual sharing, you both create an evolving, moving way to give each other pleasure, joy, and love.

FURTHER READING

Barbach, Lonnie. *For Each Other: Sharing Sexual Intimacy*. New York: Anchor Press, 1982.

Blumstein, Philip, and Pepper Schwartz. *American Couples: Money, Work, and Sex.* New York: William Morrow & Co., 1983.

Brecher, Edward. *Love, Sex, and Aging.* Boston: Little, Brown & Co., 1983.

Britton, Bryce. *The Love Muscle: Every Woman's Guide to Intensifying Sexual Pleasure.* New York: New American Library, 1982.

Comfort, Alex. *The Joy of Sex: A Gourmet Guide to Lovemaking.* New York: Crown Publishers, 1972.

Erlich, George E. *Total Management of the Arthritic Patient.* Philadelphia: J. B. Lippincott Co., 1973.

Heslinga, K. *Not Made of Stone: The Sexual Problems of Handicapped People.* Illinois: C. C. Thomas Publishing Co., 1974.

Hinton, Ann, Linda Sherby and Lynne Tenbusch. *Getting Free: Women and Psychotherapy.* New York: Grove Press, 1982.

Hotchner, Tracy. *Pregnancy and Childbirth.* New York: Avon Books, 1979.

Hurwood, Bernhardt J. *The Whole Sex Catalogue.* New York: Pinnacle Books, 1975.

Inkeles, Gordon, and Murray Todris. *The Art of Sensual Massage.* San Francisco: Straight Arrow Books, 1972.

Ladas, Alice Kahn, and Beverly Whipple. *The G Spot: And Other Recent Discoveries about Human Sexuality.* New York: Holt, Rinehart and Winston, 1982.

Lehrman, Nat. *Masters and Johnson Explained.* New York: Playboy Paperbacks, 1976.

Masters, William, and Virginia E. Johnson. *Human Sexual Response.* Boston: Little, Brown & Co., 1966.

Mooney, Thomas O., Theodore Cole, and Richard Chilgren. *Sexual Options for Paraplegics and Quadriplegics.* Boston: Little, Brown & Co., 1975.

APPENDIX A

CATALOGUES

Eve's Garden
119 West 57th Street, Suite 1406
New York, NY 10019

Frederick's of Hollywood
6608 Hollywood Boulevard
Hollywood, CA 90028

Uniquity
215 4th Street
Galt, CA 95632

Xandria Collection
P.O. Box 31039
San Francisco, CA 94131

SEXUAL BOUTIQUES

Eve's Garden
119 West 57th Street, Suite 1406
New York, NY 10019

Come to Your Senses
321 Cedar Avenue South
Minneapolis, MN 55454

Good Vibrations
3416 22nd Street
San Francisco, CA 94110

Lovecraft
63 Yorkville Avenue
Toronto, Ontario, Canada M5R 1B7

Pleasure Chest
20 West 20th Street
New York, NY 11011

APPENDIX B
Erotic Money

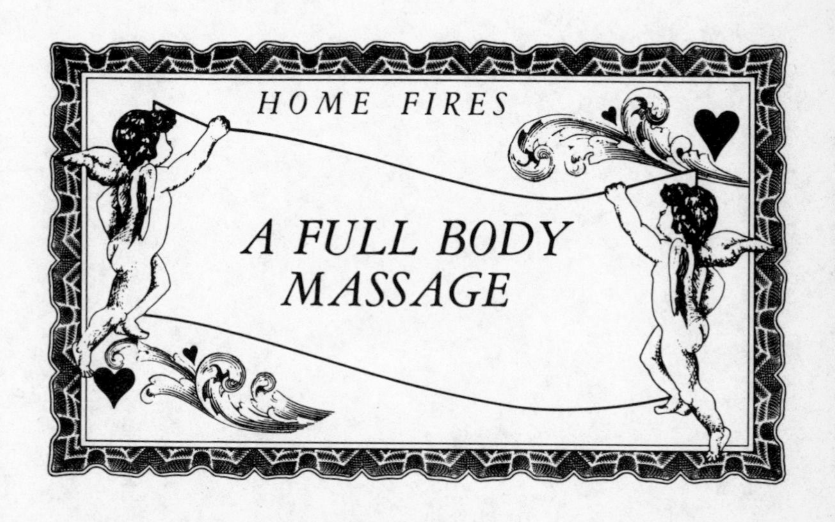

HOME FIRES
BED PICNIC

10 SLOW KISSES
HOME FIRES

HOME FIRES
BATHE ME

HOME FIRES
LET'S GO TO
A HOTEL

DANCE
WITH ME
HOME FIRES

HOME FIRES
10
MINUTES OF
STARING INTO
EACH OTHER'S
EYES

HOME FIRES
A SENSUAL
DINNER

HOME FIRES
HAVE SEX
OUTDOORS

DO A
STRIP TEASE
HOME FIRES

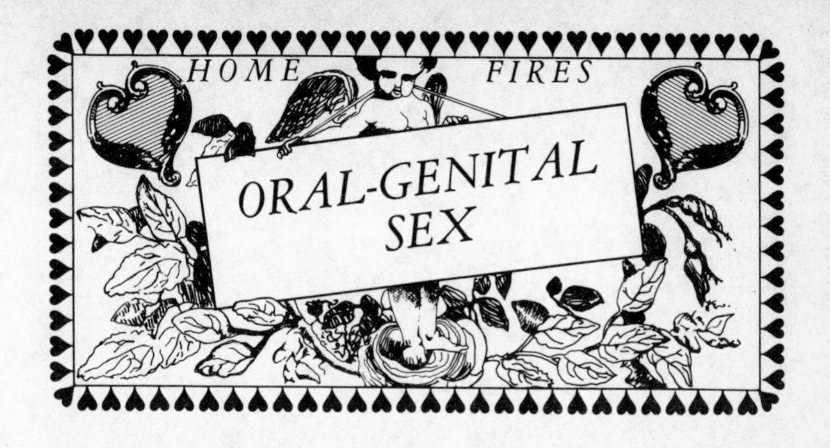
HOME FIRES
ORAL-GENITAL SEX

HOME FIRES
TELL A FANTASY

TICKLE ME WITH A FEATHER
HOME FIRES

MAKE LOVE
WITH YOUR
UNDERWEAR ON
HOME FIRES

HOME FIRES
BREAKFAST
IN BED

HOME FIRES
GO TO
A PORNO MOVIE